D1003084

PLUCKER

BY ALENA SMITH

★

DRAMATISTS
PLAY SERVICE
INC.

NOTE ON BILLING
Anyone receiving permission to produce PLUCKER is required to give credit to the Author as sole and exclusive Author of the Play on the title page of all programs distributed in connection with performances of the Play and in all instances in which the title of the Play appears, including printed or digital materials for advertising, publicizing or otherwise exploiting the Play and/or a production thereof. Please see your production license for font size and typeface requirements.

Be advised that there may be additional credits required in all programs and promotional material. Such language will be listed under the "Additional Billing" section of production licenses. It is the licensee's responsibility to ensure any and all required billing is included in the requisite places, per the terms of the license.

SPECIAL NOTE ON SONGS/RECORDINGS
Dramatists Play Service neither holds the rights to nor grants permission to use any songs or recordings mentioned in the Play. Permission for performances of copyrighted songs, arrangements or recordings mentioned in this Play is not included in our license agreement. The permission of the copyright owner(s) must be obtained for any such use. For any songs and/or recordings mentioned in the Play, other songs, arrangements, or recordings may be substituted provided permission from the copyright owner(s) of such songs, arrangements or recordings is obtained; or songs, arrangements or recordings in the public domain may be substituted.

PLUCKER was first produced at Southwark Playhouse, London, England, in 2010. It was directed by Anna G. Jones, the set design was by vPPR, and the original composition was by Elspeth Brooke. The cast was as follows:

ALEXIS .... Emily Bevan
LOUIS .... Jamel Rodriguez
LEE .... Claire Cordier
JULIAN .... Paul Westwood
THOMASINA .... Juliet Crawford

CHARACTERS

ALEXIS, a composer.

LOUIS, her boyfriend, a math teacher.

LEE, her friend, a dancer.

JULIAN, another friend, a graphic designer.

THOMASINA, Julian's girlfriend, a philanthropist.

PLACE

New York City; way, way uptown.
The living room of a one-bedroom apartment.

TIME

End of summer.
Act One: Before dinner; then after dinner.
Act Two: After dinner; later that night; the next morning.

PLUCKER

ACT ONE

Scene 1

End of summer. New York City—way, way uptown. In the living room of a smallish, rather bare, slightly faded one-bedroom apartment.

In one corner of the room, a large birdcage is covered by a cloth.

In another corner sits Alexis, in a party dress, kneeling at a little toy piano.

Offstage, from the kitchen, we hear the sound of Louis, her boyfriend, singing a cheesy, high-pitched pop song.

Alexis bangs her fist down on the keys.

ALEXIS. Oh! Life is torture!

> *Louis comes out from the kitchen, wearing an apron, and holding a wooden spoon.*

LOUIS. Something wrong?

ALEXIS. Could you keep it down in there? I'm trying to get some work done.

LOUIS. Alexis, it's Friday night. T.G.I.F. Relax.

ALEXIS. I can't—I need to focus on this—

LOUIS. Focus on me for a change! You've been focused on that all day.

ALEXIS. I got nothing done today. I can't work in this apartment!

LOUIS. Here we go.

ALEXIS. I'm telling you—it's the *noise*. We must have moved into the noisiest apartment in New York.

LOUIS. That's absurd. It's quiet in here. You're just over-sensitive.

ALEXIS. Of *course* I'm sensitive to noise, Louis. I'm a *composer*! And I'm not one of those John Cage Zen Buddhist composers who gets off on the accidental drip of the faucet, the car alarm, the clanging pipes, the wayward blast of booty bass from a neighbor's stereo! I don't find that kind of thing amusing in the least. I want to hear no sounds but my own. I'd like to be sealed off from the audible world in a private, soundless egg. I hate footsteps. I hate dogs. I want to erase everything!

LOUIS. Will you do me a favor?

ALEXIS. What?

LOUIS. Put away your piano.

ALEXIS. Put it away—you mean, right now?

LOUIS. Right now.

ALEXIS. But I'm right in the middle of—okay. I will. I will.

> *She picks up her toy piano, then hesitates.*

I don't know where to put it.

LOUIS. Just put it away.

ALEXIS. But it doesn't have a place.

LOUIS. So make a place for it.

ALEXIS. Oh, this apartment! It never feels like *anything's* in the right place!

LOUIS. What are you talking about?

ALEXIS. I feel like I'm getting waterboarded in here.

LOUIS. This is our *home*, Alexis. Stop acting like it's a torture chamber!

ALEXIS. I'm sorry. But that's what it feels like! Honestly, sometimes I don't know what attracted me to this apartment. The feng shui is all fucked up. The walls don't seem to line up straight—and something about the way the furniture's set up makes me sick! I feel like I'm undergoing some depraved psychological experiment— the kind where they wrap your extremities in cardboard and feed you meals at odd hours so your biorhythms go batshit and you never know if you're eating breakfast or dinner.

LOUIS. Really. Well—it's dinner. We're having dinner. And our friends are coming over, and when they get here, they're gonna find me in a pretty bad mood. Because you know what? You're hurting my feelings.

ALEXIS. Your—feelings?

LOUIS. Yeah. Remember how I have those?

ALEXIS. Oh, shit.

LOUIS. Yeah. I'm a big feeler.

ALEXIS. I know. You are a big feeler. And I'm being a dick.

LOUIS. Big time.

ALEXIS. Oh, man. What's wrong with me? Ever since we moved in here, I've just been—freaking out. And I don't even know why! I love you, Louis. You know that? I love you so profoundly.

LOUIS. I love you too, Alexis. I love you too.

> *They kiss.*
>
> *From the birdcage, a voice. The voice is quite loud, and quite agonized. It is the voice of Pom-Pom, a parrot.*

POM-POM. Ack! Life is torture!

ALEXIS. Uh-oh. She woke up.

POM-POM. Ack! Ack! Ack!

> *Alexis goes over to the cage and peeks underneath the cover.*

No! She's doing it again!

POM-POM. Life! Is! Torture!

ALEXIS. Hey, now! You stop that! Stop that, you hear me? That is unacceptable parrot behavior!

POM-POM. Ack! Ack!

ALEXIS. God, why won't she stop!

LOUIS. I thought if you put the cover on, she stops.

ALEXIS. Yeah, not anymore! Now she goes on doing it in the dark.

LOUIS. Well, pretty soon she'll *have* to stop. 'Cause she won't have any feathers left.

7

ALEXIS. Louis! Don't even say that! Do you understand? If Pom-Pom plucks out all her feathers, she'll die!

POM-POM. Die! Ack!

> *A green feather falls from the bottom of the cage. Alexis picks it up.*

ALEXIS. Please, Pom-Pom. Stop hurting yourself! Don't you know I love you?

POM-POM. I love you! Life is torture!

> *Another feather falls.*

ALEXIS. Oh, this is bad. This is so bad! Her poor little tummy is almost bare—and now she's moved on to her wings!

LOUIS. She's making progress.

ALEXIS. Louis! This is not a *joke*! I've had Pom-Pom since I was *six*. She's always been a bit—anxious. But since we moved here? I mean—look at her!

LOUIS. I'd rather not.

ALEXIS. You don't even care, do you.

LOUIS. It's kinda hard to care about an animal who flashes her eyes red and squawks at me every time I come within a foot of her.

ALEXIS. She's just nervous! You haven't gained her trust.

LOUIS. *Her* trust? Fuck that! She's the one who practically bit off my earlobe!

ALEXIS. I wish you were more committed to developing a healthy relationship with my bird.

> *From the futon, a cell phone rings.*

Shit—is that Julian? How'd they get here so fast? It's over an hour on the train from Park Slope—god, I wish they weren't coming tonight!

LOUIS. You were the one who made plans!

ALEXIS. Well, I felt like I had to. They've had us over so many times, and they still haven't seen our apartment.

LOUIS. So, now they'll see it.

ALEXIS. Exactly. They'll see it. And they'll judge.

LOUIS. What are you talking about?

ALEXIS. Thomasina. She won't *say* anything besides "I love your place!"—but really, that's not what she's thinking. She would never *say* what she's thinking.

Alexis picks up the phone, still ringing. She looks at the number.

Oh—it's not Julian. It's Lee.

LOUIS. Who's Lee?

ALEXIS. *(Picking up.)* Hey, Lee! How's it going—huh? Oh, no. Oh, that *sucks*.

LOUIS. What's happening? Who is that?

ALEXIS. *(Shushing him.)* Wait, so—what? You're right down the *street*?

LOUIS. What's going on? Who are you talking to?

ALEXIS. Well—you should come over here! No—I can't go out. Because, we're having a dinner thing. But—you should come! We have plenty of—totally. No, seriously. *(Slightly hushed.)* No—really, I can't go out. But—come. You know where we—? Yeah, that's right. So just come! Okay, see you in a few!

She hangs up.

That was Lee.

Beat. Louis glares at her.

Lee. The girl I've been—*Lee*. My new *collaborator*. The dancer? I was rehearsing with her last night, Louis. And the night before.

LOUIS. Oh, right—the one you "rehearse" with till three A.M., then come home stoned out of your mind. Lee. Good old Lee.

ALEXIS. That's right. Lee.

LOUIS. She's coming over?

ALEXIS. She has to come over. It's an emergency.

LOUIS. What's the emergency?

ALEXIS. She needs a place to crash.

LOUIS. What's wrong with her place?

ALEXIS. She had to evacuate.

LOUIS. What—she got a bomb threat?

ALEXIS. No. She got bedbugs.

LOUIS. Oh, great. Definitely let her sleep here then. Great! That's just great.

ALEXIS. Are you saying I shouldn't have invited her?

LOUIS. We don't want bedbugs, do we?

ALEXIS. No—but she can't sleep on the street!

LOUIS. I don't get it. You hardly even know this girl. Why is she calling you for help?

ALEXIS. As a matter of fact, we've gotten super close. That's what happens when you *collaborate* with someone.

LOUIS. I don't like how you use that word.

ALEXIS. And besides, she was in the neighborhood.

LOUIS. Who the hell just happens to be around here on a Friday night? What does she do, like, ride obscure bus routes for fun?

ALEXIS. No. She has a bike. And she'll be here in five minutes. Do you want me to tell her she can't come in?

LOUIS. Whatever. Who cares. Let this random new friend of yours sleep over. Let her move in—why not? It'll be just like *Three's Company*—the episode where they get bedbugs.

ALEXIS. Well, we'll just have to hope for the best. Which is either A) we don't get bedbugs, or B) if we do, one of them crawls up Thomasina's butt and then they get bedbugs too! Ha!

LOUIS. Nice, Alexis. Really nice.

ALEXIS. Oh, Lou. Lighten up. This is our first dinner party—we're supposed to be happy!

LOUIS. Yeah, well—fuck. Fuck! I'm not happy!

> *Beat.*

You know—all this—this crap between us—this is *not* what I was signing up for when you asked me to move in with you!

ALEXIS. When *I* asked *you*?!

LOUIS. Sorry—when you begged me.

ALEXIS. When I *what*?

LOUIS. Babe—this was your idea. Remember?

ALEXIS. Uh, *no*. Okay—maybe at first! But you were the one who got so excited about it! You got all emotional—it was like you got your period or something!

LOUIS. Uh-uh. No. Do not pin this on me. Who was the one who badgered me for *months* about ending my lease? Who threw fit after fit about the inconvenience of the commute?

ALEXIS. Okay. Some of that is coming back to me now.

LOUIS. Thank god!

ALEXIS. I did want to move in together. I admit it. But I told you there were certain conditions. Number one, I said I need space. And number two, silence! Because if I don't have silence I can't get my work done, and—

LOUIS. Yeah, yeah, and as everyone knows, when you can't get your work done your skin turns green and your hair morphs into a nest of writhing vipers.

ALEXIS. That's funny, Louis. That's funny.

LOUIS. Don't repeat yourself. You sound like Pom-Pom.

POM-POM. Ack!

LOUIS. And you know, for someone who demands so much silence, you got a noisy fucking pet. That bird never shuts up, and it doesn't bother you. But I sing a little Britney in the kitchen, you act like I'm drilling a hole in your skull.

ALEXIS. How am I dating a guy who likes Britney Spears?!

LOUIS. She's an icon!

ALEXIS. You're not even ironic about it. That's what scares me.

> *The door buzzer buzzes, meaning Lee is downstairs. Alexis goes and buzzes her in. In concert with the buzzer, Pom-Pom shrieks again.*

POM-POM. Ack!

LOUIS. My point is, Alexis, you don't hate noise. In fact, you're a noise lover! You walk down the street with your eyes closed, listening—you make hour-long detours to record the hissing from a random subway grate. You're crazy about noise! The fact is, the only noises you seem to have a problem with are any noises coming from *me*!

> *Louis exits, angrily, to the kitchen.*

Alexis throws herself down at the toy piano and plays a chord in frustration.

Scene 2

A knock at the door. Alexis jumps up to open it. Lee enters, carrying a bicycle on her shoulder.

LEE. Bedbugs, man. Not a fuckin' joke.

ALEXIS. *(Trying to block her from entering.)* Yeah—um—what a nightmare.

LEE. *(Scooting around her easily.)* I have to throw everything out. My bed. My books. All my clothes.

ALEXIS. No—can't you just wash your clothes?

LEE. It's a fucking *infestation*, dude.

ALEXIS. But what about—those clothes?

LEE. Oh—these? Nah, I'm keeping these. Gotta wear something.

ALEXIS. Yeah, but uh, are they—infested?

LEE. Shit. I don't know. Hope not.

ALEXIS. What I mean is—are we gonna—have a problem here?

LEE. Oh—you mean, if I go like this?

> *Lee starts grinding her body all up on Alexis, who squeals.*

Nah, I think you're okay. Been wearing this outfit a few days now, I haven't felt any bites.

ALEXIS. A few *days*—oh, no, Lee.

LEE. Girl, you'll be fine. Though I *did* hear they can go dormant for months. Maybe even years. You forget all about them, then one day—bam. Magical little fuckers.

ALEXIS. I don't know if it's safe for you to come in—

LEE. *(Seductively.)* You don't want me here?

ALEXIS. No—I *do* want you—I mean—uh—

LEE. Why don't we just go get a drink?

12

ALEXIS. I told you. We have friends coming over.

LEE. Who are these people? Am I gonna hate them?

ALEXIS. Julian is my best friend from college. Thomasina is his girlfriend.

LEE. *Thomasina?*

ALEXIS. I know.

LEE. Let me guess—she's rich.

ALEXIS. She's super rich. But she's nice. I mean—she *tries* to be nice. And I have to be nice to her. That big grant I was telling you about—the one I applied for? Her dad runs the foundation. And she works there. She's totally like, pulling for me.

LEE. Isn't that a conflict of interest?

ALEXIS. It's a fifty-thousand-dollar grant. I'm not asking any questions.

LEE. Yeah, you're just being nice.

ALEXIS. Yup. I'm being her friend. Even though I had so much more fun with Julian when we were single.

LEE. You should ditch them and come dancing with me.

ALEXIS. I think we did enough dancing last night.

LEE. Last night was nothing.

ALEXIS. You're a really good dancer. Everybody was looking at you—

LEE. They were looking at us.

ALEXIS. They were?

LEE. Oh, honey, I had fifteen lesbians asking me for your number.

ALEXIS. Did you tell them I'm straight?!

LEE. *(Smiling.)* I told them you're *confused.*

> Beat.

So—have you decided?

ALEXIS. Decided—what?

LEE. If you're gonna let me stay.

ALEXIS. Oh! Right. Yes, of course you can stay. But—I think you should change.

LEE. *(Flirtatiously.)* You don't like me how I am?

ALEXIS. *(Flirting back.)* I *mean*—your clothes. Why don't I get you something of mine to put on?

LEE. How's that gonna work?

ALEXIS. We'll put your clothes in a bag or something. Seal it. Cut off the air supply.

LEE. No, I mean, how's your personal style gonna work on me? I kinda have my own look going on here. I call it a postmodern dyke version of Huckleberry Finn.

ALEXIS. Oh, yeah, I can see that. Well, how about I get you something of my boyfriend's?

LEE. Hey, where is your boyfriend? I wanna check him out.

ALEXIS. Oh, he's in the kitchen. Don't take it personally if he doesn't come out. He's mad at me.

LEE. Oh—I hope it's not—because of me?

ALEXIS. No—no, it's not you. It's us. We're—well, it's not exactly domestic bliss around here.

> *From the birdcage, Pom-Pom squawks.*

POM-POM. Ack!

LEE. Hey, is that your parrot?

ALEXIS. Yes, that's Pom-Pom.

LEE. Ooh, can I see her?

ALEXIS. No, I'd rather not—

> *Lee is already at the cage, peeking under the cover. She jumps back in horror.*

LEE. What the *fuck*!

ALEXIS. I told you! She isn't looking her best these days…

LEE. What *happened* to her?!

ALEXIS. She has—problems.

LEE. Damn. And I thought bedbugs were bad.

> *Lee casually tosses her possibly infested scarf down on the futon.*

ALEXIS. Uh-oh—!

LEE. Alexis, calm down. You're not gonna get bedbugs. You're not,

okay? Because shit like this, it only happens to me. I'm telling you—
I have bad luck.

ALEXIS. Bad luck?

LEE. The worst. Wherever I go, terrible shit befalls me. Just look at
all the bad shit that's happened in only the brief time you've known
me.

ALEXIS. Like what?

LEE. Aside from the bedbugs? Let's see. Leaving my wallet on the
bus. The cell phone incident. That giant rat that fell from the sky
and hit my head on East Fourth Street. Spraining my ankle the day
of the Judson show, getting a tattoo from a drunken tattooist, oh,
and shall we add, getting bit by that homeless man's *dog*?

ALEXIS. Crap—that is a lot of stuff.

LEE. Yeah—I'm pretty sure I'm cursed. Wanna smoke this joint?

ALEXIS. Do I ever. Let's go out on the fire escape.

LEE. Cool.

> *Alexis leads Lee through the window out onto the fire escape.
> Out there, Lee lights up the joint.*

(Inhaling.) So. Marital problems?

ALEXIS. Marital. Yeah, right.

LEE. You don't think you guys will get married?

ALEXIS. I don't know! We just moved in together. I mean—let's
deal with that before we spend an afternoon smashing cake into
each other's faces for the entertainment of our remaining grand-
parents. Right?

LEE. *(Shrugs.)* I wouldn't know.

ALEXIS. You mean—you've never lived with someone?

LEE. Hell no. I need my space. That's why my girlfriend and I are
in an open relationship.

ALEXIS. Yeah—that sounds so cool. An open relationship.

LEE. Actually, it sucks.

ALEXIS. It does? Why?

LEE. Because. I want to be with other people.

15

ALEXIS. But—you get to be. Isn't that the whole point?

LEE. Theoretically. But the deal of this open relationship is that we have to tell each other everything. And if I have to tell her about it, then I don't even wanna do it. It makes everything boring, having to talk about it. And if I have to listen to one more of *her* fucking stories—ugh. I don't know. Relationships. Whatever.

ALEXIS. Yeah. Seriously.

> *Beat.*

Uh—so—did you tell your girlfriend—um. About last night?

> *Beat.*

LEE. What about it?

ALEXIS. I mean—what happened—between us.

LEE. What happened?

ALEXIS. Uh. I'm not sure.

LEE. I mean—something almost happened. But then—you stopped.

> *Alexis glances in at the living room, to make sure Louis hasn't emerged.*

This is probably a bad time to—

ALEXIS. No—it's okay. He can't hear us. He's drowning out his pain with terrible music.

LEE. Okay. Well—I'll be honest. I'm not here because of the bedbugs. I mean—I wanted to see you.

ALEXIS. Yeah. I wanted to see you too.

LEE. I mean—I want to see you all the time.

> *Beat.*

Okay, look. Obviously, we've been hanging out. A lot.

ALEXIS. Yeah. A lot.

LEE. And, obviously, we've been collaborating. So there's that whole—collaborating thing. You know. That goes on.

ALEXIS. Totally. Totally.

LEE. But last night—

ALEXIS. Yeah. Last night.

LEE. *(Softly.)* I really want to kiss you right now.

16

ALEXIS. Lee—I can't.

LEE. Why not?

ALEXIS. Because. I'm in—well, I'm *not* in—let's put it that way—I'm *not* in an open relationship.

> *Beat. Lee puts out the joint.*

LEE. So that's the way it's gonna be. Okay.

ALEXIS. Is that okay?

LEE. I guess it has to be.

ALEXIS. You seem upset.

LEE. Well, you're kind of fucking with me.

ALEXIS. Am I? I don't mean to—

LEE. Fucking straight girls. Every time.

> *Lee climbs through the window, back into the living room. Alexis follows her.*

ALEXIS. I'm not straight.

LEE. Ha!

ALEXIS. I mean—I've hooked up with girls before.

LEE. Hooked up—what does that mean?

ALEXIS. Like—kissed. In college. When I was really drunk.

LEE. Okay, let's not even have this conversation. You're straight, okay? You have a drinking problem, and you're straight.

ALEXIS. I do have a drinking problem.

LEE. Ugh. So do I.

ALEXIS. But still—you're being kind of *label*-y! I mean, sexuality is a spectrum, right? Haven't you ever had feelings for a guy?

> *Beat. Lee blushes.*

LEE. When I was younger—I had—feelings. Once.

ALEXIS. What kind of feelings?

LEE. Oh, stupid feelings. Retarded-ass I'm-falling-head-over-heels-in-love type of feelings. You know.

ALEXIS. Oh, yeah. Those.

LEE. But I was so young—I'm way too old for that now.

ALEXIS. When was this?

LEE. College. Junior year abroad.

ALEXIS. Oh, where'd you go?

LEE. Paris.

ALEXIS. That's funny. My boyfriend went to Paris. You guys can speak French together.

LEE. Yeah, probably not. Unless he wants me to order a bunch of drinks from him.

ALEXIS. You partied a lot?

LEE. *Oui.*

ALEXIS. In love in Paris—wow.

LEE. Yeah. It was—crazy. From the second I met this guy, it was just like—*bam.*

ALEXIS. Whoa.

LEE. I mean—we were twenty years old, you know? And everything is just—*sexier* when you're that age. Plus, this guy was *hot.*

ALEXIS. He *sounds* hot.

LEE. Oh, he is. Or—was. I haven't seen him since Paris.

ALEXIS. You guys didn't keep in touch?

LEE. Oh, no. Never spoke again. He left me. Total heart-shredder. I don't even allow myself to google him.

ALEXIS. Well—it sounds like one of those things that was good while it lasted.

LEE. Yeah. It was kinda like that movie *Before Sunrise*—but with a lot more blow jobs.

ALEXIS. I wish I could meet someone like that…

LEE. Dude. You have a boyfriend.

ALEXIS. I know. But I don't exactly swoon every time I see Louis.

LEE. *(Startled.)* Who?

ALEXIS. Louis. My boyfriend.

LEE. Your boyfriend's name is—*Louis*?!

ALEXIS. Uh, yeah. Hello? I've told you that before.

LEE. Have you? That is weird. That is really weird.

ALEXIS. Why?

LEE. Uh—I—no reason.

ALEXIS. Wait—was that the name of your guy?

LEE. Huh? Oh—no. Ha! No. How weird would *that* be.

ALEXIS. Ha! So what was his name?

LEE. Whose name?

ALEXIS. The guy, Lee! The guy from Paris!

LEE. *(Nervous.)* Oh—his name was—Leonardo.

ALEXIS. *Leonardo?* As in—DiCaprio?

LEE. Yeah. That's right.

ALEXIS. Could he *get* any hotter?!

LEE. *(Extremely nervous.)* Ha! Right?

ALEXIS. Shit, for a second there you had me scared. Like, what if it was Louis? But of course, it couldn't have been.

LEE. It couldn't?

ALEXIS. No. Because he didn't fall in love in Paris. He had a serious girlfriend all through college. Margot. As a matter of fact, he left Paris early because Margot got in a car accident. She wasn't hurt—but she hit someone, and they died, and it like totally traumatized her. Louis had to come back and deal with all that. Fucked up, right? And you think *you* have bad luck!

> *Alexis notices that Lee is suddenly violently scratching herself.*

Uh—Lee? Are you okay?

LEE. No. Um—no. All of a sudden—I feel really—itchy.

ALEXIS. Itchy? Okay—that's it! Take off all your clothes!

LEE. What?!

ALEXIS. Bedbugs, Lee! We need to toss your things! I mean it—strip!

LEE. No—no! I should go.

ALEXIS. Go? Like, leave? What are you talking about—I don't want you to go! You have to stay. But we can't get bedbugs. That will be like, the last straw in this apartment. So please, take your clothes off—now!

> *Lee feels like she has no choice; she strips down to her bra and boy-style underwear.*

Good. Now—I'm quarantining these. I'll go get you some jeans and a T-shirt from Louis—

LEE. No! Uh—get me a dress.

ALEXIS. A *dress*?

LEE. Or—like a skirt. And like—makeup.

ALEXIS. *Makeup?* I've never seen you in—

LEE. I want to look girly! Okay?

ALEXIS. Okay—I'll see what I can do. Be right back.

> *Alexis starts to exit, then turns back.*

Hey. Lee.

LEE. Huh?

ALEXIS. What happened last night—

LEE. Yeah?

ALEXIS. I just want you know—I liked that feeling.

> *Alexis smiles at Lee, who tries to smile back, then exits off to the bedroom.*

> *Almost immediately, Louis comes out of the kitchen.*

LOUIS. *(Entering.)* Lex! Come taste the soup!

> *Louis sees a half-naked woman in his living room and instinctively shields his face.*

Whoa—sorry! Not looking!

> *Lee looks at Louis. She is shaking.*

LEE. Oh, fuck. It's you.

LOUIS. Don't worry! I can't see you!

> *Louis sticks a hand out, with the other covering his eyes, so he has no idea in which direction to aim for a handshake.*

By the way, I'm Louis!

LEE. *(Trembling.)* Louis.

LOUIS. Can I—uh—are you—

LEE. Louis. Look at me.

LOUIS. Well, I'd feel a bit more comfortable doing that if you had more clothes on, but—

LEE. Look at my face. Picture it, oh, about ten years younger… Picture me at the top of the Eiffel Tower!

LOUIS. Oh. Oh—*shit.*

LEE. Yeah. It's me.

LOUIS. Natalie?!

LEE. Yeah. But now I just go by—

LOUIS. Lee.

LEE. Louis.

LOUIS. Fuck. We are definitely getting bedbugs.

    From the birdcage, Pom-Pom starts freaking out again.

POM-POM. Ack! Ack! Ack!

    From the bedroom, Alexis enters, holding a dress.

ALEXIS. *(Entering.)* I need to move Pom-Pom into the bedroom before too many people arrive—

    Alexis sees Louis and Lee standing there, Lee half-naked.

(Tossing the dress to Lee.) Louis! Give her some privacy!

LEE. No—uh—no. I need to go.

ALEXIS. Go? No! Was he being mean to you?

LEE. No, he, uh, really—I think it's a bad—

ALEXIS. Lee, stop. We want you to stay. Don't we want her to stay?

    The door buzzer buzzes, meaning Thomasina and Julian are
    downstairs.

POM-POM. Ack!

ALEXIS. Great. *(Sing-song.)* They're here. The Perfect Couple is here!

LEE. Can I get my clothes back? I'm gonna bounce.

ALEXIS. No! You're staying! Right, Louis?

LOUIS. No—I mean, uh—

ALEXIS. See? He wants you to stay. Now—dirty boy, leave us alone!

LEE. Oh, I don't care. He's already seen me—well. Whatever.

    Lee puts on the dress.

ALEXIS. Hot! Doesn't she look hot?

LOUIS. Uh—

ALEXIS. I'm so glad the two of you are hitting it off!

> *The door buzzer buzzes again. Alexis buzzes them in.*

Lee, prepare yourself. This is probably gonna be a boring night.

LOUIS. I don't know about that…

ALEXIS. Oh, I'll be nice! But to tell you the truth, I just wish they'd break up.

POM-POM. Ack!

> *A knock on the door. Alexis opens it. Thomasina and Julian enter, in matching jackets.*

THOMASINA. Hey, kids! Ooh, I love your place!

JULIAN. Aren't you gonna show them?

ALEXIS. Show us what?

THOMASINA. Well… look at my hand! *(Holding her breath for a second.)* We're engaged!

> *Blackout.*

Scene 3

After dinner. A haphazard arrangement of soup bowls, wine bottles, and mismatched glasses bedecks the coffee table.

The birdcage has been moved to the bedroom, offstage.

Around the table, the five of them are sprawled: Alexis, Louis, Lee, Thomasina, and Julian. They are all pretty drunk, and everybody has just finished their soup.

ALEXIS. *(In a German accent.)* "Vould it be safe to say, ze penguin is deranged!"

JULIAN. *(In the same accent.)* "Nature is vile und base! Fornication und asphyxiation! Nature ist obscenity!"

ALEXIS. *"You must never listen to zis tape!"*

LEE. What is this? What are they doing?

JULIAN. Werner Herzog.

THOMASINA. Entertaining, isn't it?

LOUIS. Is this how you guys got through four years at Oberlin? Werner Herzog imitations?

ALEXIS. And ketamine.

THOMASINA. Julian never did that.

ALEXIS. Oh, but he did. Freshman year? In the cornfield?

JULIAN. Shit. That was terrifying.

ALEXIS. College.

JULIAN. Good times.

> *Alexis and Julian high-five. Alexis sits down at her piano and plays a note or two.*

What are you working on, Lex?

ALEXIS. Same piece.

JULIAN. You're *still* working on that?

ALEXIS. Dude. It takes time. It's an *opera*.

THOMASINA. An *opera*, wow, that's amazing! I had no idea you were writing an *opera*—

ALEXIS. You didn't? But my entire grant application was about this.

THOMASINA. Oh—right. Duh. Sorry, it's been such a crazy summer—I forgot.

ALEXIS. So did you even *read* my application, or—

JULIAN. *(Interrupting.)* She read it, Lex. We talked about it. Remember, Thom? The idea is great. A giant opera about love and passion—to be played on idiotic instruments. Such as the toy piano.

LEE. Toy piano, kazoo, harmonica, bike horn—a whole bunch of junk.

THOMASINA. How do you know about it? How does she know about it?

LEE. We're *collaborating.*

JULIAN. A tragic opera played on toys. Gizmos. Ridiculous things. That's a genius idea, is what that is.

ALEXIS. Thanks, homie.

JULIAN. So when is it gonna be finished?

ALEXIS. Fuck—I don't know. I thought I'd be finished by now. But nothing's working out the way I planned. Everything's just—haywire.

JULIAN. Are you talking about your opera, or your life?

> *Beat.*

THOMASINA. Louis, that soup was delicious!

LOUIS. Thanks.

LEE. Yeah—I didn't know you could cook.

> *Beat.*

I mean—uh, she never told me.

THOMASINA. Louis is an *amazing* cook.

LOUIS. Oh, you're the amazing one. Those little pastries? Ridiculous.

THOMASINA. Oh, those are French. I took a cooking class when we were in Paris.

LEE. When were you in—Paris?

THOMASINA. Oh, in the spring. God, Paris in springtime is incredible. Seriously—you have to go.

LEE. *(Looking at Louis.)* Oh, I've—been.

THOMASINA. Oh! So then you know!

ALEXIS. Lee fell in *love* in Paris.

> *Lee's face twitches.*

THOMASINA. Did you? How romantic!

ALEXIS. She was on her junior year abroad, Lou! Just like you!

> *Louis almost chokes.*

LOUIS. Uh—really?

ALEXIS. Oh, yeah. And it sounds *so* romantic.

THOMASINA. Ooh—tell us about it!

LOUIS. Don't—

LEE. Oh, I'd be happy to. Let's see… Well, it was Paris. And we were twenty years old. And we were *crazy* in love. Like lunatics! We'd make out against the walls of stone cathedrals… we'd sleep till four in the afternoon, then go out to one of those little squares and smoke Gauloises and drink these ridiculous drinks—bellinis, I don't know—the kind of drinks only Americans on their junior year abroad ever order, I bet. The waiters were probably laughing at us. But we had no idea. We felt completely *authentic.* That's what was so beautiful about that time. I remember waking up in bed together, thinking, *this is what it means to be an adult.* But actually, we were kids. We were innocent. And we didn't have shit to do—we didn't even have class most of the time because the French students were always on strike—and all we did, all day, was amble around Parisian streets in this haze, this stupor, which was the combined effect of language immersion, too much liquor, and well—falling in love.

ALEXIS. *(Captivated.)* That's so romantic…

LEE. It hurts to think about. You know? 'Cause that time—it's just—gone.

THOMASINA. Didn't you ever see him again?

LEE. Nope. I never did.

THOMASINA. That's too bad—

LEE. Nah, you know—it's probably a good thing. People don't always age well.

Beat. Louis is red.

THOMASINA. So Lee, what do you do?

JULIAN. What do you do dot com.

THOMASINA. What?

JULIAN. That's my new thing. Whenever somebody asks some-body else what they do, I like to add, dot com.

THOMASINA. That's odd, Julian.

ALEXIS. I like it.

THOMASINA. Fine. What do you do dot com.

LEE. You're still asking me?

JULIAN. Dot org.

ALEXIS. Backslash.

THOMASINA. Will you let her answer?

ALEXIS. Sorry.

JULIAN. Dot gov.

Alexis and Julian giggle.

LEE. Uh—I'm a dancer.

THOMASINA. Oh! Like a—stripper?

LEE. No—like—contemporary—never mind. Mostly, I teach yoga.

LOUIS. *(Skeptical.)* You do?

Beat.

I mean—uh. She didn't tell me.

THOMASINA. Ooh, yoga! This is perfect! Julian, isn't this perfect? We were literally just discussing this on the way over. We're getting married on the Vineyard, okay, so we were thinking, wouldn't it be amazing to get up really early in the morning, before the craziness, and do sunrise yoga together on the beach. Just the two of us!

ALEXIS. This sounds like a Thomasina idea, not a Julian idea.

JULIAN. I'm down for sunrise yoga.

ALEXIS. When did she perform the lobotomy?

THOMASINA. You should totally do our wedding yoga! Do you have a website?

LEE. Uh—no.

THOMASINA. Oh. That's a problem.

ALEXIS. Why?

THOMASINA. I need to run every decision past my sister. And my mom. They're like my second and third in command.

ALEXIS. And where does that put Julian?

THOMASINA. Julian and I are tied for first, silly! We have *so* many choices to make… he has his hands full just trying to pick the wedding font.

ALEXIS. The wedding *font*?

THOMASINA. For the invitations, and the place cards, and everything.

JULIAN. It's a nightmare. Dot net.

THOMASINA. *(To Lee.)* He's a graphic designer, so, he obsesses.

JULIAN. I literally had a nightmare that we sent out all our invitations in Comic Sans. Or no—like, Simpsons font.

ALEXIS. Scary.

THOMASINA. Anyway—let's keep in touch about the yoga.

LEE. Nah, you don't want to hire me.

THOMASINA. I don't?

LEE. I shouldn't be a yoga teacher. I mean, sometimes I'm up there, leading the class, and I'm like, if any of you *knew* how fucked up I am, you would not be looking to me for spiritual guidance. I mean, yes, I can execute a bad-ass scorpion pose—but psychically, I am hanging on by a *thread*.

> Lee stares at Louis. He shifts uncomfortably.

ALEXIS. Scorpion pose? That sounds hot.

LEE. *(Still looking at Louis.)* Oh—it is.

> Beat.

THOMASINA. Well—Louis. The soup. Yum.

LOUIS. It's good, huh? I got the one of the moms at school.

ALEXIS. Thomasina went to Brearley. Which is where Louis teaches. He's a math teacher.

LEE. Ha! That's funny.

LOUIS. What's funny?

LEE. Oh—I just mean. The coincidence.

> *Beat.*

Anyway—what's Brearley?

THOMASINA. Um—it's a school.

LEE. Oh—is it one of those fancy schools?

THOMASINA. It's rigorous.

ALEXIS. Yes. It's fancy.

THOMASINA. If you'd been my math teacher I would have had the biggest crush on you.

ALEXIS. They all have crushes on Louis.

LOUIS. It's true. I'm like a secretary on *Mad Men* at that place. It's like nonstop sexual harrassment.

ALEXIS. Oh, but you love it.

LOUIS. Hey, those sixth-graders know how to make a man feel like a man.

THOMASINA. Well, please tell whoever gave you the recipe, that seafood soup is divine.

LOUIS. I'm glad you liked it. Some people here kept saying you wouldn't be in the mood.

ALEXIS. All I said was, it's still summer. Not exactly soup season.

LOUIS. I say it's fall. School started last week.

ALEXIS. But it's still warm outside.

LOUIS. Well, maybe you should have made dinner!

ALEXIS. Bitch, you know I can't cook.

THOMASINA. Guys, the soup was perfect. I adore seafood soup. Too bad this one can't have any.

LEE. *(To Julian.)* Are you allergic?

JULIAN. I'm vegan.

THOMASINA. He's not really a vegan. He's just a picky eater.

ALEXIS. And that's another reason I said we shouldn't have seafood soup!

JULIAN. No worries, my friends. You know I bring my own dinner.

THOMASINA. *(To Lee.)* He can't go anywhere without a Tupperware. Just one of the things I love about dating a "vegan."

ALEXIS. Correction—*marrying* a vegan!

THOMASINA. Oh, baby! We're getting married!

> *Thomasina and Julian air-kiss.*

LEE. I used to be vegan. Hardcore. Then one day, I'm walking down Bedford Ave, and I see this chick eating a hot dog. Just slamming it into her face. And it was like—bam. Fuck this. I need a hot dog.

> *Louis coughs.*

THOMASINA. *(Entranced.)* Oh, my god, I know. I'm like, obsessed with meat. I have like, meat fantasies. And I never get to eat any! Not with this one around!

LOUIS. I don't know how you do it, man. I need the flesh to survive. Beef, pork, sausages, steak… oh, man, a big bloody steak? Mmm…

THOMASINA. Louis, stop! You're turning me on!

> *Lee suddenly chokes on a sip of wine, provoking a violent coughing fit.*

ALEXIS. Lee, are you okay?

THOMASINA. Oh my god!

LEE. *(Gasping.)* I'm—no—it's—I'm fine.

JULIAN. Yikes.

THOMASINA. Well—anyway. Louis. I think you and I need to go out on a meat date. We'll go to Peter Luger's and order the biggest, juiciest steak on the menu. Alexis, you don't mind if I take your boyfriend out on a meat date, do you?

ALEXIS. Not at all. That sounds delightful. I'll stay in with your boyfriend and whip up one of those—what was that thing you just ate, Jules?

JULIAN. Tofurkey sub. With vegannaise.

THOMASINA. *Tofurkey.* Ick!

ALEXIS. *(Picking up an empty wine bottle.)* I think we're out of booze.

THOMASINA. Uh-oh. No more Pinot?!

JULIAN. We're gonna have to bounce. Tommy needs her Greege.

THOMASINA. *(To Lee, dead serious.)* I need like an I.V. drip of Pinot Grigio or else I stop having fun.

JULIAN. Or—we could bust out the crazy shit.

THOMASINA. Oh, no, Julian—you're not going to drink that.

ALEXIS. What is this crazy shit?

JULIAN. This crazy shit I bought today. In Chinatown.

THOMASINA. He won't eat a ten-dollar oyster, but he'll drink some moonshine from a blind lady on a street corner.

JULIAN. The blind lady said it's a truth serum.

LEE. Uh-oh…

THOMASINA. Ooh—do you have something to hide?

LEE. Doesn't everyone?

LOUIS. Doesn't "truth serum" just mean "alcohol"?

ALEXIS. If it's alcohol, I say bring it.

LEE. *(To Alexis.)* Are we really about to get wasted again? We got shitfaced last night.

THOMASINA. You guys hung out last night?

LEE. We *collaborated* last night.

LOUIS. There's that word again.

ALEXIS. You're such a bad influence on me.

LEE. I thought *you* were the bad influence!

THOMASINA. I didn't know you hung out last night.

JULIAN. *(Holding up the bottle.)* Okay, this shit is not fucking around. Look at this.

ALEXIS. Whoa—is that a *snake*?

JULIAN. That my friend is a cobra.

ALEXIS. What the fuck… that's awesome. Louis—look at this.

LOUIS. Weird… its eyes are open… looks like it's laughing at us!

THOMASINA. So gross. So. Gross.

LOUIS. Have you tried this shit?

JULIAN. Just got it today. Was planning to save it for a special occasion.

LOUIS. Well—this *is* a special occasion! You guys are getting married!

ALEXIS. Yeah—might as well drink the truth serum now. Find out all your dirty secrets.

JULIAN. My life is too boring for secrets.

THOMASINA. Boring? You think I'm boring?

JULIAN. Not *you*, baby.

THOMASINA. Okay. Gimme that.

    Thomasina takes the bottle, twists off the cap, and drinks.

LOUIS. *(Cheering.)* Go Thomasina!

LEE. Whoa. I'm impressed.

THOMASINA. *(Shuddering.)* Not bad.

ALEXIS. Lemme try some.

    Alexis grabs the bottle and takes a drink.

Ugh! Nasty!

JULIAN. Is it working?

LOUIS. Yeah—are you telling the truth yet?

ALEXIS. Thomasina. Anal sex. Go.

THOMASINA. Excuse me?

ALEXIS. Do you or don't you.

JULIAN. Don't answer that.

ALEXIS. Oh, shit!

THOMASINA. What a lovely dinner party this is.

ALEXIS. So are we the only ones with balls around here, or are you *ladies* gonna try some?

THOMASINA. Do it, guys. Ride the cobra.

LOUIS. *(Holding out his glass.)* Hit me up.

JULIAN. Me too.

ALEXIS. *(Pouring.)* Lee?

LEE. I don't know…

ALEXIS. Lee's acting so *prissy* tonight. Lee, what happened to you? Man up!

LEE. *(Blushing.)* I—um…

31

LOUIS. Don't make her drink it—

LEE. Oh—fuck it. Give me some.

LOUIS. *(Holding up his glass.)* To Thomasina and Julian. Congrats.

ALEXIS. Yeah, congrats, grads.

LOUIS. Getting married.

JULIAN. Yup. Pulling the plug.

THOMASINA. Julian, that's not the expression!

JULIAN. Wait—what's the expression?

THOMASINA. Tying the knot!

LOUIS. Taking the plunge?

JULIAN. Jumping into the plasma pool.

LEE. How about—taking flight?

THOMASINA. Yes! Sailing on the wings of love!

ALEXIS. Flying too close to the sun?

JULIAN. Flying solo.

THOMASINA. No—that's definitely wrong!

LOUIS. Well—congrats.

JULIAN. Hey—congrats to you guys, too.

ALEXIS. Did we graduate?

THOMASINA. You moved in together!

ALEXIS. Oh, right.

JULIAN. Bottoms up.

> *Everybody drinks. It burns.*

LOUIS. Damn!

LEE. *Intense.*

JULIAN. Tastes like lighter fluid.

ALEXIS. Nothing like lighter fluid and seafood soup.

THOMASINA. Speaking of soup, are we all finished? I'll clean up.

LOUIS. No—you don't have to do that.

THOMASINA. I don't mind!

LOUIS. No—it's our house, we'll clean up.

ALEXIS. If she wants to clean, let her clean.

THOMASINA. I actually love cleaning up. There—one of my deep dark secrets!

LEE. Bizarre.

THOMASINA. Yes, I do everything at our house, don't I baby?

JULIAN. *(Flipping through a magazine.)* Yup.

THOMASINA. Julian's one of those boys whose mommy used to follow him around picking up his socks wherever he dropped them.

ALEXIS. Are you saying you're just like his mother?

THOMASINA. God, no.

JULIAN. Hey—what's wrong with my mother?

THOMASINA. Just hand me your bowl.

LOUIS. Thom—stop.

THOMASINA. Honestly, Louis, I want to!

LOUIS. You should give Alexis some lessons.

ALEXIS. Say what now?

LOUIS. I do most of the chores around here.

ALEXIS. Hey—I swept the whole house the other day.

LOUIS. Oh, that was great. She takes out a broom, makes a big announcement: "I'm sweeping!" I come out twenty minutes later, she's blasting Mozart, lying on the floor.

ALEXIS. It was the Queen of the Night aria. I can't move while I listen to that.

LOUIS. Lying on the floor, staring at a pile of dust.

ALEXIS. You know what dust is? It's flakes of dead skin. It's death. That's what dust is.

LOUIS. You're not exactly the little housewife, is what I'm saying.

ALEXIS. Suck it.

THOMASINA. I read something today, on Goop? About the top five causes of marital problems. These are the top five issues you're supposed to confront before you get married, because they're the most likely to cause a divorce in the future.

ALEXIS. Ooh—can we guess?

JULIAN. Number one. Do we build an underground railroad in our home. Yes or no.

ALEXIS. Number two. If I become pregnant with a mouse, à la *Stuart Little*, do we abort.

JULIAN. Three. If I meet Ryan Gosling, and if for whatever reason he starts coming on to me, am I free to experiment.

ALEXIS. Four. How much of our daily life may I detail on my blog?

JULIAN. Five. Can we do it up the butt.

ALEXIS. I think you guys already sorted that one out.

THOMASINA. Do you want to hear the real list, or no?

ALEXIS. Go ahead.

THOMASINA. One. Money.

ALEXIS. That's obvious.

THOMASINA. Two. Chores.

LOUIS. That's number two? Wow.

THOMASINA. Three. Sex.

ALEXIS. *(Imitating a fat old housewife.)* They coulda made those the same category.

JULIAN. Oh, shit. Four—

THOMASINA. Four—

LOUIS. Stop. I don't care.

THOMASINA. But these are the top five marital issues—

LOUIS. But I'm not getting married. So I don't care.

　　　　Awkward. Louis stands up.

ALEXIS. Where are you going?

LOUIS. Gonna have a smoke.

LEE. *(Jumping up.)* Oh—I want to smoke.

ALEXIS. Lee—you quit.

LEE. But now I really want to smoke a cigarette.

ALEXIS. Smoking's bad for you. Don't know if you heard.

LEE. *(To Louis.)* Let's go do something bad for us.

LOUIS. *(Nervous.)* Uh—

34

JULIAN. *(Standing.)* I'm gonna smoke too.

THOMASINA. Julian! You never smoke!

JULIAN. But I like hanging out with smokers. Mind if I join you guys?

LOUIS. *(Relieved.)* Join us!

JULIAN. Can we see the stars from up here?

ALEXIS. It sounds like he's hitting on Louis.

THOMASINA. Don't let my fiancé make out with you, Louis!

LOUIS. Oh, it's gonna be sexy out there. I can't promise anything.

> *Julian smacks Louis on the ass as they crawl out to the fire escape, followed by Lee.*

THOMASINA. Shut the window! Smoking is gross!

> *Louis shuts the window. Outside, they light up. Inside, Thomasina turns to Alexis, ready for girl talk.*

So. I like your friend.

ALEXIS. Oh—yeah! Isn't she cool?

THOMASINA. Does it bother you that she's totally hitting on Louis?

ALEXIS. Um. What?

THOMASINA. Hello, she's like, drooling.

ALEXIS. That's impossible.

THOMASINA. Why? Louis is very attractive.

ALEXIS. Okay, but—she's gay.

THOMASINA. No way.

ALEXIS. Uh, yeah. She has a girlfriend. And plus— *(Lowering her voice.)* —there's kind of some sexual tension going on—between *us.*

THOMASINA. You and her?!

ALEXIS. Yeah. It's like—a thing.

THOMASINA. Okay, I did *not* pick up on that.

ALEXIS. You can't say anything. Don't tell Julian.

THOMASINA. Don't tell Julian *what*?

ALEXIS. I don't know. It's weird! Like, maybe, I'm attracted to her? But maybe I just really, really like her. I mean, I thought I was done with the part of my life where I like, make a new best friend. You know? And I feel like she and I have the potential to be, like, actually, *best friends.*

>*Beat.*

THOMASINA. Oh.

>*Slight pause.*

So she's a dancer?

ALEXIS. Yeah, she's an amazing dancer.

THOMASINA. I could have been a dancer. People always tell me I have a dancer's body.

ALEXIS. Do they? That's—good.

THOMASINA. I know.

>*Slight pause.*

Oh my god, Lexie—I missed you!

>*Thomasina throws her arms around Alexis, who is slightly unsettled.*

I missed you so much this summer.

ALEXIS. Did you? I mean—I missed you too.

THOMASINA. We were away for so long—you and I didn't have any girl time! And you've been hanging out with *her.* Have you replaced me?

ALEXIS. Oh—no, Thomasina. You are irreplaceable.

THOMASINA. I couldn't wait to come tonight and tell you our news. Were you totally floored?

ALEXIS. It was a real shocker.

THOMASINA. I know. It's so exciting!

ALEXIS. Were *you* surprised? Or were you, like, expecting it?

THOMASINA. You mean, the proposal? No—I had no idea! I mean, you know us. We're just like you guys! We've been together for ages already, and in our day-to-day lives, we were already functioning as if we were, basically, married. Right? Like we live together, we eat together, we have sex every night, we merged our record collection—

ALEXIS. *(Interrupting.)* Whoa there. Back up. You guys have sex—*every night*?

THOMASINA. Yeah—of course. Don't you?

ALEXIS. Uh—*no*.

THOMASINA. Well, I don't mean *every night*.

ALEXIS. Okay. Thank god.

THOMASINA. I mean it's not *regimented* like that. You know, sometimes we have sex in the morning—and I love doing it in the afternoon. Why? How much do you guys do it?

ALEXIS. Oh—almost that much. Yeah. Just about.

THOMASINA. You know what's crazy? We've been doing it even more since we got engaged. All I have to do is think about how I felt when Julian proposed… and it's like—do me. Now.

ALEXIS. Whoa.

THOMASINA. It was so beautiful, Lexie. That moment.

ALEXIS. Did he, like, get down on one knee?

THOMASINA. No! Oh my god, that would have looked so silly. No, it was nothing like that.

ALEXIS. What was it like?

THOMASINA. It was our last day on the Vineyard—we'd been at the beach all day. And you know that feeling you have when you've been at the beach for hours and hours—like your skin has absorbed the heat of the sun—and your mind has absorbed the crash of the waves—and you're completely relaxed—you're like, *part of the beach*—and the air is salty and fresh—and it's beginning to cool off into the evening… I was lying on my side, turned away from Julian, and there was this little girl. She was such a pretty little girl, in a blue striped suit, and I was staring at her, and all of a sudden I slipped into a dream. I was dreaming that she was my baby, our baby, and if I rolled over, Julian would be there, but he'd be older, and I'd be older, and we'd have this little girl. And then I felt Julian's hand on my back, and I turned to face him, and looked into his eyes, and he was crying. And that's when he asked me to marry him.

Silence.

ALEXIS. Wow.

THOMASINA. I know. Right?

Thomasina begins to stack up some dishes to take to the kitchen.

ALEXIS. Somehow I just didn't think Julian had it in him.

THOMASINA. I know. Wait—what?

ALEXIS. I mean, this is Julian we're talking about. The king of irony? I've been friends with him since college and I'm not sure I've ever heard him say something he actually *means*.

THOMASINA. Well—Julian's not the same as he was in college.

ALEXIS. No—I guess not.

Thomasina carries a stack of dishes into the kitchen. Alexis follows her.

Out on the fire escape, Louis and Julian are chatting. Lee is silent, gaze focused intently on Louis, who tries to ignore her.

JULIAN. So—how's cohabitation?

LOUIS. Oh—it's good. It's awesome.

JULIAN. Everyone getting along?

LOUIS. Yeah—well, except for the parrot.

JULIAN. Uh-oh. Pom-Pom's a mess, huh?

LOUIS. That parrot is fucked. Up.

JULIAN. It's so sad—she used to be so cute and sweet...

LOUIS. And now she looks like Freddy Krueger. I'm scared she's gonna attack me from inside my dreams.

JULIAN. She doesn't like you, does she?

LOUIS. We kinda have a Batman-Joker thing going on.

JULIAN. So what are you gonna do about it?

LOUIS. I don't know. Poison her food?

JULIAN. Shit, man. You let Alexis hear you talk that way?

LOUIS. Ha. Right. If she heard me say that, she'd do something worse than poison me.

JULIAN. She'd kick your ass out on the street.

LOUIS. Yeah, I got no choice. Got to put up with the plucker.

JULIAN. The things we do for love, right?

LOUIS. Absolutely.

> *Lee continues to stare at Louis, who avoids looking back at her. Julian looks up at the sky.*
>
> *Back in the living room, Alexis and Thomasina reenter from the kitchen.*

THOMASINA. So. I *love* your place!

ALEXIS. Do you?

THOMASINA. Oh, it's darling!

ALEXIS. It would be better if I had a separate work space. But I can't afford that, unless—well, unless I get that grant!

> *Beat.*

THOMASINA. Moving in together is so wonderful, isn't it?

ALEXIS. Uh—yeah. Wonderful.

THOMASINA. When Julian and I moved in together, I was just *ecstatic*. I just loved every minute of it—choosing the curtains, arranging our books, putting our toothbrushes next to each other in the bathroom. Like my toothbrush got a little buddy to keep her company.

ALEXIS. Uh—yeah. Toothbrushes.

THOMASINA. Moving in together comes first, right? And you know what comes next!

ALEXIS. I'm not sure about that…

THOMASINA. No, I get it. You're not the type of girl who's interested in weddings. Right?

ALEXIS. Hell yes I am. I've been planning my wedding since I was like six. Little sparkling lights strung up everywhere—and lanterns. Like a shit-ton of lanterns.

THOMASINA. I am so with you on that. It sounds perfect!

ALEXIS. Yeah, but the problem is—I don't think Louis believes in marriage.

THOMASINA. What! Why?

ALEXIS. Well, he certainly doesn't believe in the idea that the *man* should propose to the woman. He says it's an artifact of a patriarchal tradition where marriage was a purely economic transaction and women didn't have any agency over their lives. And what's romantic about that? It's part of his whole girl-power thing. So annoying.

THOMASINA. God, men can be such feminazis sometimes.

ALEXIS. Seriously.

THOMASINA. But you know—maybe he's just not ready. I mean—financially.

ALEXIS. Right. Wait—what?

THOMASINA. You know. It's a guy thing. They like to be really settled in their careers before they commit.

ALEXIS. They do?

THOMASINA. You know. It's a money thing. Julian was really hung up on it—even though, obviously, with my parents—I mean, we have nothing to worry about. But it mattered to him. And he's doing so well at work—and it's lucky, 'cause, you know, as soon as we get married, we'll be starting the whole baby escapade!

Alexis chokes.

ALEXIS. Um. What?

THOMASINA. Well, you know, in two years, I'll be almost thirty-two. That's already my outer limit for the first kid.

ALEXIS. The—first?

THOMASINA. I want to have three. Three look so good on a Christmas card! So we need to get started.

ALEXIS. I think I'm gonna pass out.

THOMASINA. What's wrong?

ALEXIS. You're telling me I have to have a baby in two years? You might as well tell me I have two years to *live*!

THOMASINA. You don't have to do anything! I'm just saying what I want! Just because I want to have a baby, that doesn't mean you have to!

ALEXIS. Jesus Christ. I need another drink.

Alexis picks up the cobra liquor and chugs. Thomasina picks up some glasses and goes back to the kitchen. Alexis follows.

Out on the fire escape:

LOUIS. *(To Julian.)* So—how's work?

JULIAN. Eh. You know. It's work.

LOUIS. I hear you're doing well.

JULIAN. I guess. But sometimes when I think about how much of my adult life I spend at that place, I feel like a piece of plastic tossed in the trash. Not even recycled. Just tossed.

LOUIS. Sounds like you hate it.

JULIAN. Eh. I don't know. Thing is—I make a lot of money.

LOUIS. Yeah—I know what that's like.

JULIAN. Gotta make that paper.

> *Beat.*

LOUIS. Well—this is out. Let's go in.

LEE. *(Finally speaking.)* Wait.

LOUIS. What?

LEE. I want another.

LOUIS. Oh—okay. Here.

LEE. No. Don't go in. Smoke it with me.

LOUIS. *(Looking at Julian.)* Uh—

JULIAN. It's cool. I'll leave you two alone.

LOUIS. No—uh—

JULIAN. Don't worry about it. It's cool. I want to say hi to the bird.

> *Julian goes in through the window, leaving Louis and Lee outside, alone.*
>
> *Just as Julian is shutting the window, Thomasina and Alexis come back in from the kitchen.*

THOMASINA. *(Seeing Julian.)* Baby, you're back!

JULIAN. *(In a silly voice.)* Hiiii guuuyyyyss.

ALEXIS. Had enough of the secondhand smoke?

JULIAN. Lex, can I go in your room?

ALEXIS. Yeah, sure—she likes you. Just—be quiet with her, okay?

JULIAN. Shh.

Julian exits. Thomasina wipes some crumbs off the futon. She finds a green feather stuck in the crease and holds it up. Alexis takes the feather from her and strokes it sadly.

Meanwhile, out on the fire escape:

LEE. My teeth are aching.

LOUIS. Why?

LEE. I'm so excited to see you.

Louis moves toward the window, but Lee is blocking him, and won't move.

LOUIS. I want to go in.

LEE. I'm gonna start to cry.

LOUIS. Don't. She'll—they'll hear you.

LEE. Then don't go inside.

Louis backs off, unwillingly.

In the living room:

ALEXIS. So—he's doing well at work?

THOMASINA. Oh, incredibly.

ALEXIS. What about his book?

Thomasina looks blank.

His *book*. His graphic novel.

THOMASINA. Oh, that. He's not working on that.

ALEXIS. Why not?

THOMASINA. He doesn't really have time.

ALEXIS. He should make time.

THOMASINA. Well, maybe he'll get back to it someday.

ALEXIS. He better get back to it. That book is the bomb. I mean, it *looks* amazing—but also, I feel like it really says something. About us. How we live today. And I mean, if you're not saying something about how we live today, then what the fuck are you doing?

THOMASINA. *(Uninterested.)* I don't know. He was always depressed when he was working on that book. And half the time he wasn't even working. He was just—staring at it.

ALEXIS. So now he's not depressed?

42

THOMASINA. No—not at all. I mean, thank god for Prozac. And also, now he's so excited about the wedding! It gives him something to design that he actually cares about. We're having so much fun. We agree on everything—and it's going to be perfect! Well—except for one problem.

ALEXIS. What's the problem?

THOMASINA. Francine.

ALEXIS. Julian's mother?

THOMASINA. I could stab that woman in the throat.

ALEXIS. Wow—tell me how you really feel!

THOMASINA. Alexis, you don't understand. She's so fucking *involved*! She wants to butt in on everything. I'm like, Francine, it's not your *job* to plan this wedding. I already *have* a mother, thanks, and *my mother* will plan this wedding! It's supposed to be the *bride's* family who's in charge—and no offense, but in this case, we're the ones with the money! So why not just let us do it? But she's like, oh, I don't have a daughter, and this is my only chance, and please let me help, blah blah. And I'm like oh my *god* if this woman has *any say* in this event the whole thing will go down in flames! She has *such* bad taste, Alexis. It's like a sick joke how bad her taste is, honestly. And my mother has perfect taste! And so does Julian, actually, which is one reason why I'm in love with him, but how somebody with perfect taste could have emerged from Francine's tacky womb is a total mystery. My sister says that all of Julian's taste has been formed in direct opposition to his mother and that's how it happened. But now it's like there's no escaping from her. She's like Ursula the fucking sea witch, and she keeps popping up out of the ocean and trying to drown me. Every word that comes out of her mouth is completely insane. Like—she keeps talking about a *pot luck*. I'm sorry, a POT LUCK WEDDING?! Can you *imagine*?! Like I'm going to send out invitations that say, hey, come to our wedding, and bring along a bucket of mac and cheese! Like hey, you know, why bother having a wedding at all! Why don't we just have a fucking *tag sale*? But she just keeps going on and on about how a friend of hers gave her kid a pot luck wedding, and it was so *inclusive*, and the whole *neighborhood* came, and you know, of course they saved

43

lots of money. I'm like, Francine, we aren't *concerned* about money. But she won't drop it! She's such a *fucking Jew*!

ALEXIS. *(Aghast.)* Thomasina!

THOMASINA. Look, I'm allowed to say that. I'm one-quarter Jewish.

ALEXIS. I—wow. I don't know. That's—um. I don't know.

THOMASINA. Alexis, have you *met* this woman? Would *you* want her planning your wedding?

ALEXIS. Well, if I was marrying Julian—

> *Awkward beat.*

I mean—she's his *mother*. She's part of who he is.

THOMASINA. You have to help me.

ALEXIS. Help you?

THOMASINA. Say something to Julian. Tell him he has to set boundaries here. Tell him how upset she's making me!

ALEXIS. Geez, for a second there I thought you were gonna propose an internment camp.

THOMASINA. Don't tempt me.

ALEXIS. But—what do you want me to say? I mean, it's his *family*…

THOMASINA. All you have to say is, look. These are our choices. His and mine. Not hers. Will you just say that to him? Please? He'll listen to you. Alexis, you're our best friend.

ALEXIS. Okay—I'll say—something.

THOMASINA. Thank you, Lexie. Thank you *so much*.

> *Thomasina gathers up one last round of dishes, and heads for the kitchen. Alexis follows.*
>
> *Outside:*

LOUIS. I'm done standing here in silence.

LEE. *(Reaching for his hand.)* Louis—

LOUIS. *(Snatching his hand away.)* I don't know what you think you're doing here.

> *Beat.*

All night—staring at me—flirting—like you think something's gonna happen. What do you think is gonna happen?

LEE. I—I just—

LOUIS. You just. Need. To go.

>*Beat.*

Look—I'm sorry. But the fact is—

LEE. Oh, what are the *facts*, Louis? Tell me. As a matter of *fact*, I have no idea what you think the facts are, here. I only know one fact, myself. The fact that you broke my heart.

LOUIS. Shh—

LEE. Oh, yeah, let's keep it down. Let's not let anyone hear the truth about you. Imagine if she found out! She thinks you're this—this—*boyfriend*—who asks her how her day was, who putters around in the kitchen, making *soup*! Imagine if she knew the real you! The one who destroyed me!

LOUIS. Oh, come *on*. I wasn't that bad.

LEE. You were a complete and total asshole, Louis. And apparently, you still are.

LOUIS. How was I an asshole? I never lied to you. You knew the whole time I had a girlfriend—

LEE. Yeah, well that didn't stop you from—Jesus Christ. Boys!

LOUIS. Look, I'm not really interested in replaying this scenario—

LEE. I hate you. I seethingly hate you. I hate you from the soles of my feet.

LOUIS. Then why don't you leave?!

LEE. Because! This is *destiny*. We've been thrown back together in the most insane way—

LOUIS. But how insane is it, really?

LEE. What?

LOUIS. Come on. You must have known.

LEE. Known *what*?

LOUIS. You must have—come on. You're telling me this is a coincidence?

LEE. Are you accusing me of—

LOUIS. Hey. All I'm saying is, you're the one who apparently hasn't been able to stop thinking about me for ten years.

LEE. Oh, don't *flatter* yourself—

LOUIS. Look. We can meet up next week or something. We can have coffee, or something—

LEE. Fuck you!

LOUIS. Shh!

LEE. You think I came here to find you? After what you did to me—trust me, Louis, I never wanted to see you again. But this is the kind of shit that happens to me. I run into the guy who hurt me worse than anyone ever has—and I still—

LOUIS. You still what?

LEE. I still—feel something.

> *Beat.*

LOUIS. You always did have bad luck.

> *Beat.*

LEE. Louis—it's been ten years, and I show up out of nowhere. Aren't you a little bit excited to see me?

LOUIS. I can't be excited to see you.

LEE. Why not?

LOUIS. Because. It's against the rules.

LEE. I can see why you're a teacher. You love to act like you have all these rules. And then the next thing you know, we're having oral sex in a garden at Versailles.

LOUIS. Yeah—and then we're getting stung by a horde of bees.

LEE. Oh, it was worth it.

LOUIS. You're crazy.

LEE. And that's what you love about me.

LOUIS. You can't stay here tonight.

LEE. Why? You afraid of what might happen?

LOUIS. *Nothing* is going to happen. You can't be in my house— with my girlfriend—all over me—we're not in Paris anymore!

LEE. You had a girlfriend then, too.

LOUIS. Well, I'm different now.

LEE. Are you?

LOUIS. I'm in a serious relationship. And we don't cheat on each other.

LEE. Ha—right.

LOUIS. Excuse me?

LEE. She cheated on you last night. With me.

Louis takes a step back.

LOUIS. So. You haven't changed either.

LEE. What?

LOUIS. Homewrecker.

Blackout.

End of Act One

ACT TWO

Scene 1

The very next moment. Inside, Alexis enters from the kitchen. She sits down at the toy piano. Then, Julian enters, from the bedroom.

JULIAN. She's asleep.

ALEXIS. You didn't wake her?

JULIAN. No. I was very quiet.

Thomasina enters from the kitchen.

THOMASINA. Hiiiii guuuuyyyyysss.

Lee suddenly climbs in through the window. Louis stays outside.

ALEXIS. *(To Lee.)* What were you doing out there, chain-smoking?

Lee says nothing. She exits off towards the bedroom.

(Calling after her.) Lee? *(To the others.)* What was that? Was something going on out there?

JULIAN. Seemed like they were trying to have a private conversation.

ALEXIS. But—they don't even know each other.

JULIAN. I was getting the private conversation vibe.

ALEXIS. Should I go out there?

THOMASINA. Wait—no! I'll go. I need some air. And you two need to talk.

JULIAN. We do?

THOMASINA. You haven't seen each other all summer! You have a lot to catch up on. Talk. I'll go out and ask about this mysterious private conversation.

JULIAN. Cool—Alexis can play me some Mozart.

ALEXIS. Thom—wait—

48

THOMASINA. Yes?

ALEXIS. Um—I feel kind of awkward—but, there's something—kind of important—but—I don't know if I'm allowed to ask.

THOMASINA. Oh! No. Don't feel awkward. I know what you're going to say.

ALEXIS. You do?

THOMASINA. Of course. I know—I've been avoiding the subject all night.

ALEXIS. Yeah, I noticed…

THOMASINA. Well, on my way over here I was like, am I gonna tell Alexis tonight? And I wasn't planning to, but—we might as well just get it out in the open.

ALEXIS. Uh-oh. This doesn't sound good.

THOMASINA. Oh, Lexie! I don't want you to be sad about this.

ALEXIS. Fuck. Okay. Who is it. Who'd you pick? Who's better than me?

THOMASINA. It's not that she's better—honestly—it's just—we decided it should just be my sister!

ALEXIS. Your *sister*?

THOMASINA. Yeah, we just decided to keep it in the family. You can understand that, right?

ALEXIS. Uh—*no*. No, I don't understand. Isn't that like a *severe* conflict of interest?

THOMASINA. Conflict of—what?

ALEXIS. Okay, no offense, but it's kind of *weird* to give this huge honor to someone who's *in* your immediate family. It just doesn't look right!

THOMASINA. But Alexis—that's what weddings are all about. I mean, ultimately, weddings are about *family*!

ALEXIS. Weddings? Wait—what are you talking about?

THOMASINA. What are *you* talking about?

ALEXIS. I was asking who got *picked*—

THOMASINA. Who I picked to be my maid of honor!

ALEXIS. Maid of—oh my god, no! I was talking about the *grant*!

THOMASINA. The—oh.

ALEXIS. Yeah, you know—the life-changing *grant* I applied for? Geez, you thought I'd be that upset about not getting to be a bridesmaid?!

THOMASINA. Well—I guess not.

>*Beat.*

ALEXIS. Uh—I mean—I'd love to be a bridesmaid! Or a—best man. Whatever!

>*Beat.*

JULIAN. *(In a sing-song.)* Mis-un-der-staaaan-diiinnnggg…

ALEXIS. Well—anyway—about the grant—have you heard anything?

THOMASINA. *(Coldly.)* The grant. Not really. I haven't even been to the office in like two months.

ALEXIS. Do you know if—I'm—a finalist?

THOMASINA. Alexis, I'm really not supposed to say anything. It's unprofessional.

ALEXIS. Okay, can you *please* just tell me if I'm a finalist?

THOMASINA. Okay. Duh. You're a finalist.

ALEXIS. I *am*?!

THOMASINA. Now can we please stop talking about this? If my dad knew I was saying anything to you, he'd be super pissed off.

ALEXIS. Thomasina—

THOMASINA. Yes?

ALEXIS. Just—thank you.

THOMASINA. You're so welcome. Now—I'll leave you two alone, so you can *talk*…

JULIAN. Wait—babe.

THOMASINA. Yeah, babe?

JULIAN. Will you scratch my back? I have an itch right—there.

THOMASINA. Sure, babe.

JULIAN. Ahh. That's better.

Thomasina kisses Julian.

Louis enters from the fire escape.

THOMASINA. Louis! I was just about to join you—

ALEXIS. Long time no see.

LOUIS. Hey. I'm out of smokes. Going for a walk.

Louis goes toward the front door.

THOMASINA. You want company?

Louis says nothing.

He wants company. I'll go with him. You kids have fun without us!

Thomasina and Louis exit, out the front door.

Alexis and Julian are left alone. Julian picks up the "truth serum."

JULIAN. Another shot?

ALEXIS. Oh in*deed.*

Julian pours; they drink.

She was really asleep? That's good. She hasn't been sleeping at all. We used to sleep alone, you know? And she doesn't like sharing the bedroom with Louis. She wants me all to herself again.

Beat.

JULIAN. Lex—you doing okay?

ALEXIS. I don't know.

Beat.

I've been having heart palpitations.

JULIAN. That doesn't sound too good.

ALEXIS. Yeah. All I do is worry about beats and measures, and meanwhile my own heart can't keep it together.

JULIAN. You should go to a doctor. It could be serious—

ALEXIS. Don't say that. It's not serious. It's stupid. I move in with my boyfriend and my heart stops working. Have you ever heard anything stupider than that?

Alexis sits down at her piano and plays a note.

I just want to hear something *clear—sustained—*without any interruptions. And this apartment—keeps interrupting! Every sound I hear is just—distortion. I don't know. Maybe I wasn't ready for this. But it happened. Ready or not. It all happened—the whole *moving process*—the parade of activities lined up and went by in some kind of chronological order—or was it just one exhausting, momentous explosion? Yesterday, I lived alone. Now I live here, with Louis. Blink. Blink.

> *Beat.*

JULIAN. Well—I know something that's gonna work out.

ALEXIS. What's that?

JULIAN. You're gonna get the grant.

ALEXIS. What?!

JULIAN. Don't tell her I told you. But yeah. You're gonna get it.

ALEXIS. Oh my god. Oh my god, oh my god! Julian—this is—this is *everything*!

JULIAN. Congratulations, dude.

ALEXIS. Oh my god—Jules—this is *it*. This is the universe, patting me on the back. This is the freaking cosmos giving me a high-five! Saying, it can *happen*. If you just keep working, and don't let anything stop you, it really *can happen*!

JULIAN. Yeah. Sometimes.

> *Beat.*

ALEXIS. I heard you stopped working on your book.

> *Beat.*

JULIAN. Why are you bringing that up?

ALEXIS. 'Cause—why? It's so good.

JULIAN. That's not what anyone else appears to think.

ALEXIS. What do you mean? Everyone thinks it's amazing.

JULIAN. Not agents. Not publishers.

ALEXIS. You haven't even shown it to anyone—

JULIAN. Actually, I showed it to two agents. And they both said no.

ALEXIS. Oh, come on. Two agents? Who cares? You're gonna let two rejections stop you? Julian, do you even *realize* how many times I've been rejected—

JULIAN. I don't want to talk about this.

ALEXIS. I'm just saying—

JULIAN. Alexis? Stop.

> *Julian picks up a magazine and flips through it. Alexis sits in silence at her piano.*
>
> *Julian puts down the magazine.*

Guess it's time for us to go. I've looked at all the magazines in your house.

ALEXIS. Jules—I'm drunk. You know I'm just blathering on about stuff cause I'm drunk. That's all.

> *Beat.*

It's been so long since we got to hang out—by ourselves. Like old times. We always hang out as couples now. We never bro down.

> *Beat.*

Anyway—listen—I just want to say—congratulations.

JULIAN. Thanks, friend-o.

ALEXIS. Are you totally psyched?

JULIAN. About getting married? Yeah, I'm pumped.

ALEXIS. Are you gonna play Jock Jams at your wedding?

JULIAN. To get the crowd pumped? Totally.

ALEXIS. This is such a weird phase of life we're in. Don't you think?

JULIAN. No weirder than any other.

ALEXIS. It's like—we're at this point, right now, where we're making these—choices. And the choices we make will determine the ultimate structure of the piece. But you can't know the ultimate shape of a thing when you're just beginning to create it. You have to do all this guesswork. And right now, right here, these choices we're making are like—vulnerable. Indeterminate. We could still break off, go in a different direction, do something—unexpected. But whatever we do, our future depends on it. Everything is about to get, like, totally *determined.*

> *Beat.*

JULIAN. Well, I guess we just have to kind of—go with the flow.

> *Beat.*

ALEXIS. Julian, can I ask you something?

JULIAN. Shoot.

ALEXIS. Okay, please take into consideration the fact that I'm wasted.

JULIAN. Uh-oh.

ALEXIS. What it is is, okay—how come you and I never got together?

JULIAN. What?

ALEXIS. I mean, can we just pose the question? Now that you're getting married and everything. Because on some level—I've thought about it. Haven't you?

JULIAN. Um—I don't know. I mean, we're friends.

ALEXIS. Yeah, exactly. We're friends. We get along. We like each other. So how come we never—fell in love?

JULIAN. We made out once.

ALEXIS. We did?

JULIAN. Alexis! We totally made out—freshman year?

ALEXIS. Oh—right! Oh, my god, that got blacked out.

JULIAN. So—we tried it. Didn't happen.

ALEXIS. But our lives could be so different now if—it had.

JULIAN. Yeah. You wouldn't be with Louis.

ALEXIS. And you wouldn't be with Thomasina.

JULIAN. So—things worked out.

ALEXIS. I guess. But—why? Why do things go one way when they could have gone another?

JULIAN. Honestly? You want to know why I never tried to date you?

ALEXIS. Tell me.

JULIAN. Because. You scare me.

ALEXIS. What?

JULIAN. You scare me. On that level. And I've always thought—Louis is the only guy I know who isn't scared of you. And that's why you two are together.

54

Beat.

ALEXIS. Well. It's no wonder I scare you.

JULIAN. What?

ALEXIS. Honestly? Julian—you're kind of a wimp.

JULIAN. Excuse me?

ALEXIS. Look—I know you're in love with her. But I need to say this. I need to say it to you now so I don't have to stand up at your wedding and say it in front of everyone. I think you gave up on yourself when you met Thomasina. And I think she let you give up. There are things about you—important things—that Thomasina is never going to accept. And you've let her pick and choose. It's like she got to pluck out the parts of Julian she likes, and throw away the parts of Julian she doesn't like. You used to be made up of all these parts—and now you're—simpler. You let her simplify you. But I miss the old Julian. I miss the complicated Julian—the one who wasn't toned down, airbrushed, streamlined—the one who wasn't so fucking *happy all the time*!

Silence. Julian's face is bloodless. He picks up the "truth serum."

JULIAN. I guess this stuff works.

The door opens. Louis and Thomasina enter.

THOMASINA. *(Brightly.)* I mean of course I'm a feminist, but, you know—whatever.

LOUIS. Uh-huh.

THOMASINA. *(Seeing Julian.)* Baby—you look like you're gonna be sick! *(Rushing to him.)* Oh, no. It's all my fault. I told Alexis to say something about your mother.

JULIAN. About—what about my mother?

THOMASINA. You mean you didn't have the conversation?

JULIAN. What conversation?

Just then, Lee enters. She's wearing a different, sexier dress, bright red lipstick, and heels.

ALEXIS. Lee—holy crap. What are you wearing?

LEE. I got dressed up. This is a party, right? Where's the music? I wanna dance!

55

THOMASINA. *(Happy for the distraction.)* Ooh—dance party!

> *Lee presses play on Louis's iPod, which is plugged into some speakers. A dance remix of a super-cheesy pop song comes on.*
>
> *Lee starts grinding Alexis, making sure that Louis is watching.*
>
> *Thomasina gets excited and starts grinding with Louis.*
>
> *Louis, halfheartedly dancing, notices that Julian looks quite pale.*

LOUIS. Hey, man—you really don't look so good—

JULIAN. Yeah—I feel sick—

LOUIS. Maybe it's that snake liquor!

THOMASINA. Oh, no. It's the Tofurkey!

JULIAN. I don't think so—

THOMASINA. It's the Tofurkey for sure. You can't eat that stuff anymore, baby! We're gonna have to talk about changing your diet.

LOUIS. You need to lie down or something?

JULIAN. I just—I need to get out of here. I'm—I'll see you guys.

> *Julian rushes out the door. Louis stops the music.*

THOMASINA. Well, time to go. I have to comb that little boy's hair and put him to bed.

LOUIS. Is he okay?

THOMASINA. Oh, he'll be fine. He has stomach issues. Just one of the things I love about him! Anyway—so great to see you guys. So fun. So. Fun. And I *love* your place!

LOUIS. You know how to get back to the train?

THOMASINA. Oh, it's late—we'll just take a cab.

LOUIS. A cab from here will be pretty expensive…

THOMASINA. Oh, I know, it's terrible, but—I can't get back on the subway. We'll just jump in a cab. *(To Lee.)* You live in Brooklyn, right? We're going to Park Slope. You want to ride with us?

LEE. Oh—uh, I have my bike…

ALEXIS. Lee's staying here tonight.

LOUIS. No—

THOMASINA. She *is*?

ALEXIS. Well, she can't go home.

THOMASINA. Why not?

ALEXIS. Because. She got bedbugs.

> *Beat.*

THOMASINA. You got—bedbugs?

LEE. Yeah. Lame, huh?

THOMASINA. She has *bedbugs*, and you let her come over? And then you let *us* come over, without—wow. That's—wow. Thanks for letting us know, you guys. Thanks a lot.

LEE. I'm sure you won't get bedbugs—

THOMASINA. Do you realize—okay. Wow. That is so inconsiderate. Okay. We have to go.

> *From the bedroom, the sound of Pom-Pom, louder and more agonized than ever.*

POM-POM. *(Offstage.)* Ack! Ack! Ack! Ack! Ack!

LOUIS. Jesus Christ.

ALEXIS. Pom-Pom! I better go check on her—Thomasina, congrats again—great seeing you—Lee, come with me.

> *Alexis pulls Lee with her, off to the bedroom.*
>
> *Thomasina and Louis stand there.*

THOMASINA. I don't know how you can stand living with that bird.

> *Blackout.*

Scene 2

A few minutes later. Louis sits on the futon, staring at the bottle of truth serum. He takes a swig.

Alexis comes out of the kitchen holding a bottle of cleaning fluid and a rag.

She sprays a spot on the table in front of Louis and wipes it off. He appears not to notice.

ALEXIS. Look, honey. I'm being a good little housewife. I'm cleaning.

> *Louis says nothing.*

Look—sparkling.

> *No response.*

Okay—what's with the silence?

> *Silence.*

Louis? What's wrong?

LOUIS. Why don't you tell me?

ALEXIS. Tell you what?

LOUIS. Why don't you tell me what you did last night. *(Beat.)*

ALEXIS. What I—what did she—oh, god.

LOUIS. So it's *true*?!

ALEXIS. What's true?

LOUIS. Alexis, did you cheat on me last night? With her?!

ALEXIS. No! I mean—I don't know.

LOUIS. What—you don't remember?

ALEXIS. No, I mean, I don't know if what I did could really be considered cheating.

LOUIS. Well, why don't you tell me what you did and I'll let you know.

ALEXIS. Okay—all that happened was, we went out dancing…

LOUIS. Uh-huh.

ALEXIS. At this totally underground lesbian party in Bushwick—

LOUIS. Oh, cool. Very cool.

ALEXIS. And I was *wasted*—

LOUIS. Wonderful.

ALEXIS. And we—sort of—kissed.

LOUIS. You *kissed* her?!

ALEXIS. For like two seconds! At which point I *instantly* pulled away, ran to the train, and came home. Dude, this is *not* a big deal. Hello, do you remember last New Year's? You made out with that random woman *and* her husband!

LOUIS. We were on *mushrooms*!

ALEXIS. So? I was drunk!

LOUIS. And they were both like forty-five, and *Dutch*, and you were *there*, and it was *weird*, and I didn't have feelings for either of them! It was meaningless!

ALEXIS. Well, this was meaningless too!

LOUIS. Are you sure?!

　　　Beat.

I can't believe you invited her here. She can't stay here tonight!

ALEXIS. No. She can't.

LOUIS. She needs to *go*!

ALEXIS. Yes, yes, you're right! I don't know what I was thinking— I'll tell her she has to go—as soon as she stops crying.

LOUIS. What do you mean—crying?

ALEXIS. Hysterics. I don't know what it's about. I tried to get her to tell me but she couldn't string a sentence together.

LOUIS. God, what the FUCK IS THAT WOMAN DOING IN OUR APARTMENT?!

ALEXIS. Louis! Shh!

LOUIS. I don't want her here, do you understand? I want her out. Out!

ALEXIS. Okay, okay! She'll go! I don't want her here either—it was a dumb mistake—I have zero interest—I regret the whole thing! But she's a perfectly nice person—

LOUIS. She's a freak.

ALEXIS. Excuse me?

LOUIS. I mean—she freaks me out.

ALEXIS. But—why?

LOUIS. She—reminds me of someone.

ALEXIS. Of who?

LOUIS. Just this—girl. This girl who like—stalked me.

ALEXIS. *Stalked* you? When?

LOUIS. In college.

ALEXIS. While you were dating Margot?

LOUIS. Yeah. And she knew I was in a relationship. She just didn't care. She had no respect for anything.

ALEXIS. But so—what happened between you?

> *Beat.*

LOUIS. I—slept. With her.

ALEXIS. What?! You *cheated* on Margot?! You never told me that!

LOUIS. It's not something I like to talk about!

ALEXIS. You said Margot cheated on you!

LOUIS. Not exactly. She dumped me and started dating this business major forty-eight hours later. But first—I cheated on her. So I deserved it. I was an asshole. I hurt her, terribly.

ALEXIS. You mean—the girl?

LOUIS. No—I mean Margot!

ALEXIS. It sounds like you hurt this other girl.

LOUIS. *(Viciously.)* Who cares about her?

ALEXIS. Um—I think you're supposed to care about people you sleep with. I think.

LOUIS. You're supposed to care about your girlfriend. Or boyfriend. That's who you're supposed to care about.

ALEXIS. It's so weird that you never told me this…

LOUIS. Well, it was a big fucking mess. Okay? And that's why I'll never, ever do it again. I am one hundred percent opposed to cheating. Of any kind. Unlike *you*, when I'm committed to someone, I'm committed.

ALEXIS. Unlike *me*? What does that mean?

LOUIS. It means, I don't go around—being *unclean*.

ALEXIS. *Unclean?* Okay, what is this, the Bible?

LOUIS. We're supposed to be monogamous.

ALEXIS. I don't see a ring on my finger.

LOUIS. A ring—okay, what is this, the fifties?

ALEXIS. I'm just saying—

LOUIS. *I'm* just saying, you did something that I would not have allowed myself to do! You broke the rules! And you can tell me that it doesn't matter, you can tell yourself that, but it *does* matter. It has an impact. It hurts.

> *Beat.*

ALEXIS. Oh my god, Lou! I'm so sorry! What is wrong with me? It's like I'm actually *trying* to destroy our relationship. Like I can't stop myself! God, I'm such an idiot—

LOUIS. Yeah, well—I must be an idiot too.

ALEXIS. Why do you say that?

LOUIS. Because I love you. Idiot.

> *Beat.*

ALEXIS. Louis, listen to me. All I want—*all I want*—is for this—us—to work. For us to be happy.

> *Beat.*

LOUIS. It's good to hear you say that.

ALEXIS. I mean it. Louis—I love you. I've never loved someone like this. I've never been so—close. And—it scares me. Because if I lost you—I'd lose *myself.*

LOUIS. I feel the same about you.

> *Beat.*

ALEXIS. Guess what.

LOUIS. What.

ALEXIS. I got the grant. Julian told me.

LOUIS. Guess what.

ALEXIS. What?

LOUIS. I already know. Thomasina told me.

ALEXIS. Lou—this is gonna make everything better. You'll see.

LOUIS. Will it?

ALEXIS. Yes. I won't have to work here anymore. I'll get a studio. And this can just be—our home. Yours and mine.

> *Beat.*

LOUIS. Look at you. You're incredible, you know that?

ALEXIS. Me?

LOUIS. Yeah, you. You're amazing. You're the kind of woman I tell the girls at school they can be. You're brilliant, and beautiful, and you believe in yourself. And now look—the world believes in you too.

ALEXIS. Oh, Louis. You're just—the best.

LOUIS. You're so sexy when you win prestigious awards. I want you…

ALEXIS. Oh—gosh—

LOUIS. Mmm—I want you so bad…

ALEXIS. Oh—that feels—

LOUIS. Shh… just relax, baby… relax…

ALEXIS. Wait—Louis—

LOUIS. Come on… it'll feel so nice …

ALEXIS. But I'm not—I don't—

LOUIS. Shh… just let me—

ALEXIS. No—Louis—ow! Stop! Please—just stop!

LOUIS. Fine! God damn it!

> *He jumps up and heads out.*

ALEXIS. Wait—where are you going?

LOUIS. I'm not welcome in here!

ALEXIS. You *are* welcome—I just don't feel like *doing it*—

LOUIS. You *never* feel like doing it!

ALEXIS. That's not—

LOUIS. When was the last time?

ALEXIS. What?

LOUIS. In this apartment. How many times have you and I done it, since we moved into this apartment?

ALEXIS. Look—don't make it about counting. You know I hate when it all becomes about counting—

LOUIS. Yeah, well, this ain't about counting shit—because there ain't shit to count! Many ancient numerical systems wouldn't even have a *concept* for how many times we've had sex here, 'cause it ain't a number! It's a zero!

ALEXIS. This is what I get for dating a math teacher.

LOUIS. So now you're gonna start picking on my job?! Oh, I'm sorry I don't make a shit ton of money like *Julian*.

ALEXIS. What does that have to do with anything?

LOUIS. I don't know! You tell me!

ALEXIS. Louis—we can't have this conversation right now—

LOUIS. Yeah, well, too bad! This is the conversation we're having!

ALEXIS. I don't even know what we're talking about—

LOUIS. We're talking about the fact that we never *fuck*!

> *Beat.*

ALEXIS. I—I just—

LOUIS. You just *what*?!

ALEXIS. I just feel—anxious.

LOUIS. Alexis, you just won a fifty-thousand-dollar grant. What do you have to feel anxious about?

ALEXIS. I don't know.

LOUIS. Right.

ALEXIS. Okay, fine! Here it is. I'm upset about Thomasina and Julian.

LOUIS. What about them?

ALEXIS. You know—the whole marriage thing.

LOUIS. Can't you just be happy for them?

ALEXIS. It's not them. It's us.

LOUIS. What about us?

ALEXIS. How come they're getting married, and we're not? You know? How come they get to be so sure about where their relationship is going? We've been together just as long—and where is our relationship going? Louis, I'm twenty-nine years old. And by the time I'm thirty-five, I want to be married. And I want to have a baby. At least I think I do. I'm like ninety-nine percent sure I do. No, I do. I do. And I'm with you. So I need to know that that's what you want, too.

LOUIS. Alexis, you won't even let me touch you, and now you want me to get you pregnant?

ALEXIS. I just want to know that we're going somewhere!

LOUIS. We just moved in together!

ALEXIS. Look—I'm not asking you to *propose*. But I need you to do something. I need you to make a pledge.

LOUIS. A pledge?

ALEXIS. Yes. I need you to be clear about what your intentions are. I need you to tell me where you see us going in the future. And if I don't get that from you—well, I'm not sure I can stay in this relationship.

> *Beat.*

LOUIS. Okay. You can have it.

ALEXIS. What?

LOUIS. A pledge. Sure. I pledge to you that I want to spend the rest of my life with you.

ALEXIS. Do you—mean it?

LOUIS. Yes! I mean it! I want to be with you, Alexis. Now, and always. So—is that what you want?

> *Beat.*

I said, *is that what you want?*

ALEXIS. *(In a tiny voice.)* I don't know.

LOUIS. What?

ALEXIS. I don't know. I don't know! I don't know if that's what I want!

> *Beat.*

LOUIS. You know what? You're fucking crazy.

Beat.

You're so fucking crazy, Alexis, nobody but me would ever be able to put up with you. Nobody. Because you're a child. A child who sits here, playing with toys—like everything is a joke. Your whole conception of love is a fucking joke! An opera for toy piano—yeah, I get it. Ha ha. Ridiculous. Stupid. Stupid!

> *Louis grabs the bottle of cleaning fluid and turns to exit.*

ALEXIS. *(Extremely upset.)* Where are you going?

LOUIS. I'm going to clean up.

ALEXIS. No—not in the bedroom!

LOUIS. There's bird blood and feather dust everywhere. It's disgusting.

ALEXIS. But you can't spray that stuff anywhere near her—not in her condition! You know how sensitive she is to those fumes? Louis—that stuff could kill her!

LOUIS. And what a *shame that would be*!!

> *Louis exits to the bedroom. A door slams.*
>
> *Before Alexis can go after him, Lee enters from the bathroom. She's wearing her own clothes again, and has evidently just washed her face after crying.*

LEE. I'm gonna go.

> *Beat.*

Sorry I barged in on you. It was a mistake for me to come.

ALEXIS. Oh—no—it's—my fault. I'm the one who's been making all the mistakes.

> *Lee goes to her bicycle and fiddles with the lock.*

LEE. Well—thanks for dinner.

ALEXIS. Oh, sure. I hope you enjoyed the soup.

LEE. Oh—ha. Yeah.

> *Beat.*

By the way—I see what you mean about her.

ALEXIS. About who?

LEE. Thomasina. She's irritating. Typical rich girl bullshit. And do you see how she hits on Louis?

ALEXIS. On—Louis?

LEE. Oh my god, she's all over him. Like, complimenting him, and flirting with him—

ALEXIS. Oh, that's just—the dynamic. It's like a joke between us— we flirt with each other's boyfriends.

LEE. Well, I don't see you flirting with her boyfriend. But she's *all over him*.

ALEXIS. Really?

LEE. Oh, yeah. And oh my *god*, all that stuff about weddings, and babies—like oh, babies, babies, babies, nobody else in the whole world is more obsessed with babies than me! Well, you know what? *I'm* obsessed with babies!

ALEXIS. You are?

LEE. Uh—yeah! I have baby fever!

> *Lee kicks her bike, hard.*

ALEXIS. Lee—are you okay?

LEE. No. No, I'm not.

ALEXIS. Look—if this is about last night—

LEE. It's not about last night. It's not about *you*!

ALEXIS. Oh—okay. So—why were you crying?

LEE. I was crying because—I'm a loser!

ALEXIS. What?

LEE. I'm almost thirty years old. I'm broke. My fifth metatarsal's all fucked up. I can't afford to go to the doctor. I can't afford to even *think* about having a baby! I can't even sleep in my bed tonight because the very religious Mexican family I live with found my freaking *vibrator* in their bathroom—

ALEXIS. Wait a minute. What?

LEE. Yeah, I get awoken from my alcoholic coma at four P.M. today by Señora Sanchez banging open my door, eyes covered, screaming "Los muchachos! Mira! They see! Todo el mundo! The children! The children!" And she's waving my *purple fucking dildo* in the air. Her kids found it in the bathroom. I left it there. BECAUSE I WAS DRUNK!!! So now I need to find a whole new living situation—

ALEXIS. Lee—hang on. I'm confused. What about—the bedbugs?

LEE. Oh. Right. I said that.

ALEXIS. Yeah—you said that.

LEE. Um. That was a lie.

ALEXIS. There are no bedbugs?

LEE. No. It was a vibrator. But you see why I can't go home!

ALEXIS. Um—yeah.

LEE. I'm a loser, Alexis. In the eyes of Señora Sanchez, in the eyes of the world. I'm a pathetic, broke-ass, fucked-up lesbian *vagabond*—and the worst part is—the worst part is—

> *Slight pause.*

How do I even know that I'm gay?

ALEXIS. What?! You mean, you don't *know*?

LEE. My girlfriend says—if I could fall in love with a guy—then I probably will, again. But what if it was just—him? You know? What if *he* was the one?

ALEXIS. You mean—Leonardo?

LEE. Who?

ALEXIS. Leonardo! From your junior year abroad!

LEE. Oh—right. Him. Yes, *him*! You know—what if I found him again? Maybe—shit! I don't know! Half of me just wants to go back in time and be twenty years old again. But the other half is like, *no. You're an adult!* I just want to be an adult—like, with *money*. And a *wife*. Or—husband. Whatever. Dude, I don't know. *How do people do it?!* Why can't I figure it out? I just want what you have, Alexis! I'm so jealous of your relationship!

ALEXIS. Well, that's ironic.

LEE. Why?

ALEXIS. Because—sometimes I just wish I was single.

LEE. You do?

ALEXIS. I just want to go to a party by myself again. You know? I want to have a crush on someone again! You know how it is—when you set your sights on someone. Maybe it's at a show, maybe he's playing guitar, and looking dark and melancholy, and you say to yourself—that's him, he's it, and I am going to get with him. Tonight. And even though the room is full of other perfectly attractive women who might be thinking the exact same thing, at this precise moment you kind of light up, and you know you have it in you to make it happen. Tonight. You know that strange, cosmic needles are weaving you and him together with burning threads of fire. You know that he will be unable to resist you. And it's true. You stick it out till three in the morning, drinking and smoking way too many cigarettes, talking to other guys you're not the slightest bit attracted to, watching him flirt with other girls, but always catching your eye at the last possible second before you were about to give up, letting you know with one hot glance that it's on, he just has to get rid of this one and then he'll make his way over to you. And then he does, he makes his way over to you, and he puts his hand on the small of your back, and you feel calm, safe, protected, even though you are going up in flames. And this is what you give up when you settle down. You give up this crazy magic that it took you years to perfect. It's like an arrow-maker having to put down his tools and stop making arrows. No more setting your sights on someone. No more sending fiery arrows zooming through the dark.

> *Beat.*

I just want to meet someone again who sets me on fire. You know? Like your guy. The guy from Paris.

LEE. Alexis—for fuck's sake. The guy in Paris—was *Louis*. That was Louis!

> *Alexis stares at Lee, in shock.*

> *Louis enters, from the bedroom. He's holding a large green feather.*

LOUIS. I have some bad news.

> *Alexis turns to look at him, speechless.*

She totally freaked out on me. And—pop. Out it came. This was the biggest feather she had left.

> *Beat.*

Is everything—okay in here?

Beat.

ALEXIS. I need to sleep alone with her tonight.

LOUIS. With—who?

ALEXIS. With my bird.

> *Beat.*

She needs me.

LOUIS. But—I need you.

ALEXIS. Do you understand what happens to parrots when they pluck out all their feathers? They eviscerate themselves. They plunge their beaks into their own hearts.

> *Beat.*

LOUIS. You're telling me to sleep out here—with her?

> *Beat.*

ALEXIS. Look—it's okay with me.

LOUIS. *What's* okay with you?

ALEXIS. It's okay with me if you want to sleep with Lee.

> *Beat.*

Give me that feather. I'll put it with all the others.

> *Alexis takes the feather from Louis and goes into the bedroom.*
>
> *Louis and Lee just stand there for a second.*

LOUIS. Typical.

> *Beat.*

She makes me do all the dirty work.

> *Beat. Then, Louis heads for the front door.*

LEE. Where are you—going?

LOUIS. I'm leaving.

LEE. Don't.

LOUIS. I have to.

LEE. But—we haven't even gotten to—

LOUIS. To what?

LEE. To—see each other.

> *Beat.*

LOUIS. You look the same.

LEE. I do?

Beat.

LOUIS. *(Obviously resisting an urge.)* I gotta go.

LEE. Fine. I'll come with you.

LOUIS. No. We're not doing this.

LEE. I remember things you said to me. Like—I remember—

LOUIS. Stop.

Beat.

I'm not up for a stroll down memory lane right now. I'm dealing with some shit right here. In the present.

LEE. Well—I'm here too.

Beat.

And what—am I just supposed to forget? Is it supposed to have slipped my mind—that you were the first person who told me I was beautiful? That your hands were the first to encircle my—as if you were—*shaping* me? Well, I'm sorry, but of all the moments in my life, you and me on that balcony in Paris is up there with the most unforgettable.

Beat.

And now you're going to leave again—just like you did back then. As if it never happened. Admit it! Why can't you just admit it—we were in love!

Beat.

LOUIS. You don't even know me. You have this imaginary version of me—and it's really just *you*. Not me.

LEE. No. You just can't handle the fact that I see you the way I see you. That I have an impression of you and it's *mine* and it *is* you and it's the you I *keep* and you can't take it away from me. Ever. And the way *she* sees you—it's different. I have my own you. And nobody else will ever get their hands on it.

Beat.

LOUIS. I have to go.

LEE. Why?

LOUIS. Because—she's kicking me out. I built the nest. She moved in. And now she doesn't want me.

LEE. But Louis—I want you.

> *Louis suddenly goes over to Lee and kisses her. They kiss passionately. Blackout.*
>
> *In the darkness—the sound of a song played on a toy piano.*

Scene 3

> *The next morning. Bright and cheerful. Some morning sounds from the street. Lee is asleep on the futon. Louis is nowhere to be seen.*
>
> *Lee wakes up, stretches, yawns, rubs her eyes and looks around. Just then, the front door opens. Louis enters.*

LEE. Hey. Where'd you go?

LOUIS. Went for a walk. Couldn't sleep. Here.

> *He tosses her a brown paper bag.*

LEE. What's this?

LOUIS. Got you a croissant.

LEE. Chocolate. Nice.

LOUIS. I remember you liked that kind.

> *Beat.*

LEE. Well—I should get out of here.

LOUIS. So that's it, huh?

LEE. Uh—did you want to—talk? Or something?

LOUIS. No, that's cool. Fuck and run.

LEE. Oh, like that's something you know nothing about.

> *Beat.*

LOUIS. Look—I know I hurt you. But—you have to understand,

okay? You struck a chord in me. You made me feel like my whole life could be different.

Beat.

But then I'd be kissing you and I'd see her face. When she got in the accident—I thought it was my fault. Like I had caused it somehow—by being with you.

Beat.

And now here you are again—after all these years. And I'm in another relationship. I'm always trying to make it work and then you show up and you—unleash something in me.

Beat.

Okay. Now you say something.

Beat.

LEE. This is a good croissant.

Lee and Louis smile.

Suddenly, from the bedroom, a scream. A terrible scream.

Alexis comes out from the bedroom, as if from a nightmare.

ALEXIS. She's dead. Pom-Pom is dead. Oh, life is torture!

Louis gets up, stares at her for a second, and then walks out of the apartment.

Alexis watches him go.

(*Quietly, to herself.*) He never really cared about her.

Beat. She sits down at her toy piano. She runs her finger across the top of it.

She used to perch right here, on the piano. She loved to feel the music. Her bones are like straws—thin and hollow. Can you imagine if you had bones like that, how good the music would feel?

Lee, awkwardly, comes up behind Alexis and puts a hand on her back. Alexis flinches.

You knew. Didn't you.

LEE. Knew what?

ALEXIS. You came here to find him. You were—using me.

LEE. No—that's not true.

ALEXIS. Why should I believe you? You lied about the bedbugs.

LEE. Alexis, I swear to god—when I walked in here last night, I came for *you*. I had no idea I was gonna find—him.

ALEXIS. But you were obsessed with him.

LEE. Well—he's the one guy who ever—touched me. There.

ALEXIS. *(Afraid.)* Where?

LEE. In that—marrying place.

> *Beat.*
>
> *A knock on the door.*

ALEXIS. Louis?

> *Alexis goes to the door and opens it. Thomasina enters. She's wearing a raincoat and high rubber boots. Her hair is wrapped in a scarf.*

Thomasina—what are you doing here?

THOMASINA. *(Curtly.)* Your neighbor let me in. Julian's waiting downstairs. Good morning.

LEE. Is it raining?

THOMASINA. No. It's a beautiful day. This is because of the bedbugs.

> *Alexis and Lee exchange a glance.*

ALEXIS. Why doesn't Julian come up?

THOMASINA. We're in a rush. I just came to get my ring.

ALEXIS. Your ring?

THOMASINA. My engagement ring. I took it off last night while I was doing the dishes. Didn't you find it?

ALEXIS. No—I haven't seen it.

THOMASINA. I left it right by the sink.

> *Thomasina goes to the kitchen, being very careful not to touch anything that might be infested.*
>
> *As Thomasina exits, Lee turns to Alexis.*

LEE. Um. I'm gonna take off.

> *Beat. Then, Thomasina bursts out of the kitchen.*

THOMASINA. You stole it! You stole it, didn't you! Just like you want to steal *everything* from me!

ALEXIS. What are you talking about?!

THOMASINA. Julian told me what you said last night.

ALEXIS. Oh. Uh-oh.

THOMASINA. Yeah! Uh-oh! And now I can't find my ring!

ALEXIS. I didn't take your ring, Thomasina, I swear!

THOMASINA. Oh, so what happened? Your *parrot* ate it?!

> *Alexis bursts into tears.*

LEE. Uh—the parrot's—dead.

THOMASINA. Dead?!

LEE. Died last night.

THOMASINA. Well. I didn't know that. But what I do know is, if that ring is not back on my finger in point five seconds, I'm calling the *police!*

ALEXIS. *(Through sobs.)* I don't have it, I swear!

LEE. Here. I have the ring.

> *Lee pulls Thomasina's ring off her own finger, where it has been the whole time. Thomasina and Alexis look at her in shock.*

I took it. Last night.

> *Thomasina snatches it from her.*

I'll probably never get a ring like that. And I thought it looked good with my outfit.

> *Lee exits, with her bicycle. Thomasina turns to Alexis.*

THOMASINA. This is what happens when you make new friends on *Craigslist.*

ALEXIS. I told you I didn't take it! I can't believe you accused me—

THOMASINA. Oh, I'm *sorry*, Alexis. I guess it was crazy of me to think that you would *ever* do something like that. You would never take my ring. Just like you would never talk behind my back—and you would *never* tell Julian to break up with me!

ALEXIS. I—

THOMASINA. Stop. He told me everything. In fact we got in a giant fight about it, the entire ride home. And we have *never* gotten in a fight! Thanks to what you said, he's completely freaking out. He says the wedding feels too conventional—that he doesn't want to be on a schedule—that maybe we should just *elope*! Elope?! Can you imagine?! And this is all your fault. And the worst part is—the worst part is—

ALEXIS. What?

THOMASINA. You were my best friend!

Beat.

I wanted you to be my bridesmaid. It was just going to be my sister, and my cousin, and you. I don't have a lot of friends, Alexis. I know it's hard for you to understand. But I don't. And our friendship was—important to me. And now—I can't even invite you to the wedding. If we even *have* a wedding!

Beat.

I thought about calling my dad today. I thought about telling him not to give you the grant. But then I decided—no. You deserve it. You deserve to see what it's like when you choose your art over all the relationships in your life.

Beat.

I just don't get it. All I've ever been is nice to you. I've tried so hard—I *fought* for you. And this is what I get? Why do you hate me, Alexis? What did I do to you?

ALEXIS. You—replaced me.

Beat.

THOMASINA. Well.

Beat.

I just have one last thing to say. If you wanted to cheat on Louis, you didn't need to come on to your *friend*. You could have just done what I did.

ALEXIS. What did you do?

THOMASINA. I fucked a cab driver. He was from Turkey, and it was fantastic. And if you *ever* tell Julian that, I will get that grant money taken away. I promise you that.

Thomasina turns to the door.

Just as she's going out, Louis comes in.

Thomasina brushes past him, and exits.

ALEXIS. Louis! You're back! Now we can talk—

LOUIS. No. It's over, Alexis.

Beat.

It's over. I'm moving out.

Beat.

And it's so sad.

Beat.

It's so sad, because—I love you. I love you—and I don't want to do this. And it's gonna take me a long time to get over you.

Beat.

We were so close—so close. And you kept asking me about the future. But you didn't want me *now*. In the present. And that hurt me so much.

Beat.

ALEXIS. *(Clutching her chest.)* My—heart—

LOUIS. Are you okay?

ALEXIS. It's like—a flutter. Like—a mistake.

LOUIS. Just—calm down—

ALEXIS. I can't. I can't. *(Beat.)*

LOUIS. You'll be okay. Now that you have that money, you can afford to live here by yourself. You won't even need a studio.

Beat.

ALEXIS. Louis—

LOUIS. Yeah?

Alexis, awkwardly, gets down on one knee.

ALEXIS. Will you marry me?

Louis stares at her. Then, he turns and exits out of the apartment.

Alexis looks down at the floor. She sees one of Pom-Pom's large green feathers. She picks it up, and strokes it.

There is a knock on the door. It opens. Julian enters.

JULIAN. Hey. This is for you.

Julian hands Alexis a small, wilted flower.

I'm sorry about your bird.

ALEXIS. *(Taking the flower.)* Oh—thanks.

JULIAN. I picked it out of a downstairs window—hope the neighbors won't mind.

ALEXIS. They'll be so happy not to hear Pom-Pom shrieking, they probably won't even notice.

Beat.

JULIAN. Look—all that stuff you said to me last night—

ALEXIS. I know. I shouldn't have said it.

JULIAN. But I needed to hear it.

Beat.

And it means a lot. That you care so much about me. That you care about my work.

Beat.

You always believed in me more than anyone else. And I've always trusted your judgement because, I don't know—you get it. You just get it.

Beat.

But last night you said some things that made me think—she doesn't get it.

Beat.

The thing is—I love this woman. I know she's not perfect. I know our relationship isn't perfect. And I don't care if it is because—I love her. She makes me happy.

Beat.

And that doesn't mean that you and I couldn't—I mean—I don't know. I care about you. A lot. If there was some way for us to stop time and go off to a foreign country, just to try it out—well. Who knows?

Beat.

But that's not how life works. You don't get to try out every option.

You don't get to sit there writing "I love you" in a thousand different fonts.

Beat. Alexis smiles.

Okay, that was a really bad metaphor.

Beat.

You know what I'm saying, Lex? It's weird. This *is* a weird phase of life. Making all these choices. But in a way—you don't get to choose. You don't have any choice at all about who comes into your life. All you can do is open the door and let them in.

Beat.

ALEXIS. Sometimes I walk by music, playing in a window. And all of a sudden I can feel myself, not walking by the window, but inside it. And there's a man there, and he's the man of my life, and we're listening to this simple piece of music. And we're happy. And it makes me happy—to think of that.

Beat.

JULIAN. She's waiting for me down there. I gotta go.

He offers his fist to Alexis for a fist bump.

Bros?

ALEXIS. *(Fist-bumping.)* Before hos.

JULIAN. I'll g-chat you, okay?

Alexis nods. Julian exits.

Alexis looks around at the apartment. She goes over to the toy piano and kneels in front of it. She lays the feather and the flower down on top of the piano, silently.

ALEXIS. *(To herself.)* Nice and quiet.

Silence.

End of Play

PROPERTY LIST

(Use this space to create props lists for your production)

SOUND EFFECTS

(Use this space to create sound cues lists for your production)